It's another great book from CGP...

Maths exams can seem daunting — especially if you're not sure what to expect.
But they're less stressful if you've done plenty of realistic practice in advance.

Happily, this book (which includes a **free** Online Edition)
is packed with exam-style questions to fully prepare you for the real thing.
We've even thrown in practice exams with online video solutions.

How to get your free online extras

Want to read this book on your computer or tablet?
Just go to **cgpbooks.co.uk/extras** and enter this code...

3448 4296 0887 1963

By the way, this code only works for one person. If somebody else has used
this book before you, they might have already claimed the online extras.

CGP — still the best! ☺

Our sole aim here at CGP is to produce the highest quality books —
carefully written, immaculately presented and dangerously close to being funny.

Then we work our socks off to get them out to you
— at the cheapest possible prices.

Contents

☑ Use the tick boxes to check off the topics you've completed.

Section Five — Angles and Geometry

Section Six — Measures

Section Seven — Statistics and Probability

Practice Papers

How to get answers for the Practice Papers
Your free Online Edition of this book includes a link to step-by-step video solutions
for Practice Papers 1 & 2, plus worked solutions you can print out.
(Just flick back to the previous page to find out how to get hold of your Online Edition.)

Published by CGP

Editors:
Katherine Craig, Kirstie McHale, Sarah Oxley, Sam Pilgrim,
David Ryan, Megan Tyler, Rachel Ward.

Contributors:
Andrew Ballard, Terence Brown, Pamela Chatley, Rosie Hanson, Claire Jackson.

With thanks to Ceara Hayden and Mark Moody for the proofreading.

ISBN: 978 1 84762 980 7

Groovy website: www.cgpbooks.co.uk

Jolly bits of clipart from CorelDRAW®
Printed by Elanders Ltd, Newcastle upon Tyne

Based on the classic CGP style created by Richard Parsons.

How to Use This Book

- Hold the book <u>upright</u>, approximately <u>50 cm</u> from your face, ensuring that the text looks like <u>this</u>, not sıɥʇ. Alternatively, place the book on a <u>horizontal</u> surface (e.g. a table or desk) and sit adjacent to the book, at a distance which doesn't make the text too small to read.

- In case of emergency, press the two halves of the book together <u>firmly</u> in order to close.

- Before attempting to use this book, familiarise yourself with the following <u>safety information</u>:

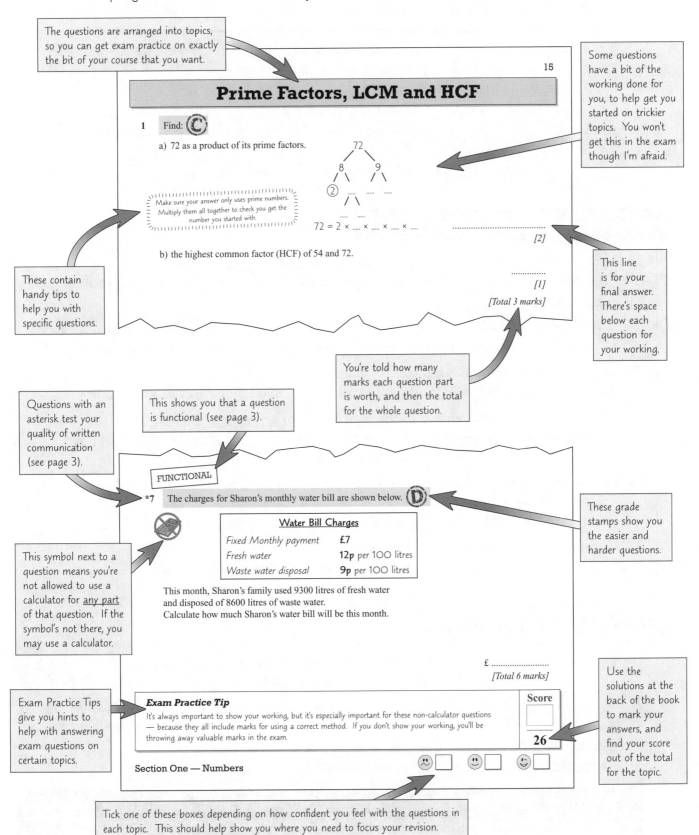

The questions are arranged into topics, so you can get exam practice on exactly the bit of your course that you want.

Some questions have a bit of the working done for you, to help get you started on trickier topics. You won't get this in the exam though I'm afraid.

These contain handy tips to help you with specific questions.

This line is for your final answer. There's space below each question for your working.

You're told how many marks each question part is worth, and then the total for the whole question.

Questions with an asterisk test your quality of written communication (see page 3).

This shows you that a question is functional (see page 3).

This symbol next to a question means you're not allowed to use a calculator for <u>any part</u> of that question. If the symbol's not there, you may use a calculator.

These grade stamps show you the easier and harder questions.

Exam Practice Tips give you hints to help with answering exam questions on certain topics.

Use the solutions at the back of the book to mark your answers, and find your score out of the total for the topic.

Prime Factors, LCM and HCF

1   Find: **C**

a) 72 as a product of its prime factors.

> Make sure your answer only uses prime numbers. Multiply them all together to check you get the number you started with.

72 = 2 × ..... × ..... × ..... × .....

....

[2]

b) the highest common factor (HCF) of 54 and 72.

....
[1]
[Total 3 marks]

FUNCTIONAL

*7   The charges for Sharon's monthly water bill are shown below. **D**

Water Bill Charges

Fixed Monthly payment	**£7**
Fresh water	**12p** per 100 litres
Waste water disposal	**9p** per 100 litres

This month, Sharon's family used 9300 litres of fresh water and disposed of 8600 litres of waste water.
Calculate how much Sharon's water bill will be this month.

£ ....
[Total 6 marks]

Exam Practice Tip

It's always important to show your working, but it's especially important for these non-calculator questions — because they all include marks for using a correct method. If you don't show your working, you'll be throwing away valuable marks in the exam.

Score

26

Section One — Numbers

Tick one of these boxes depending on how confident you feel with the questions in each topic. This should help show you where you need to focus your revision.

Exam Tips

OCR Exam Stuff

1) If you're studying the OCR linear course (Mathematics B) you will have <u>two</u> exams — one <u>calculator</u> exam and one <u>non-calculator</u> exam.

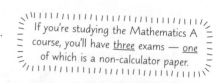
If you're studying the Mathematics A course, you'll have <u>three</u> exams — <u>one</u> of which is a non-calculator paper.

2) Both exams are <u>1hr 30mins</u> long and both are worth <u>100 marks</u>.

3) Timings in the exam are really important, so here's a quick guide...

- Each paper is worth <u>100 marks</u> and you've got <u>90 minutes</u> to complete the paper, so you should spend <u>less than a minute per mark</u> working on each question (i.e. spend less than 2 minutes working on a 2 mark question).

- If you have any time left at the end of the exam, use it to <u>check</u> back through your answers and make sure you haven't made any silly mistakes. <u>Not</u> to just stare at that hottie in front.

- If you're totally, hopelessly stuck on a question, just <u>leave it</u> and <u>move on</u> to the next one. You can always <u>go back</u> to it at the end if you've got enough time.

There are a Few Golden Rules

1) **Always, always, always make sure you <u>read the question properly</u>.**
For example, if the question asks you to give your answer in metres, <u>don't</u> give it in centimetres.

2) **Show <u>each step</u> in your <u>working</u>.**
You're less likely to make a mistake if you write things out in stages. And even if your final answer's wrong, you'll probably pick up <u>some marks</u> if the examiner can see that your <u>method</u> is right.

3) **Check that your answer is <u>sensible</u>.**
Worked out an angle of 450° or 0.045° in a triangle? You've probably gone wrong somewhere...

4) **Make sure you give your answer to the right <u>degree of accuracy</u>.**
The question might ask you to round to a certain number of <u>significant figures</u> or <u>decimal places</u>. So make sure you do just that, otherwise you'll almost certainly lose marks.

5) **Look at the number of <u>marks</u> a question is worth.**
If a question's worth 2 or more marks, you're not going to get them all for just writing down the final answer — you're going to have to <u>show your working</u>.

6) **Write your answers as <u>clearly</u> as you can.**
If the examiner can't read your answer you won't get any marks, even if it's right.

Obeying these Golden Rules will help you get as many marks as you can in the exam — but they're no use if you haven't learnt the stuff in the first place. So make sure you revise well and do <u>as many</u> practice questions as you can.

Using Your Calculator

1) Your calculator can make questions a lot easier for you, but only if you <u>know how to use it</u>. Make sure you know what the different buttons do and how to use them.

2) If you're working out a <u>big calculation</u> on your calculator, it's best to do it in <u>stages</u> and use the <u>memory</u> to store the answers to the different parts. If you try and do it all in one go, it's too easy to mess it up.

3) If you're feeling reckless, and decide to do a question all in one go on your calculator, use <u>brackets</u> so the calculator knows which bits to do first.

REMEMBER: <u>Golden Rule number 2</u> still applies, even if you're using a calculator — you should still write down <u>all</u> the steps you're doing so the examiner can see the method you're using.

You Need to Understand the Command Words

Command words are the words in a question that tell you what to do.
If you don't know what they mean, you might not be able to answer the questions properly.

Calculate...   This means you'll have to work something out — either using pen and paper OR your calculator.

Work out...   This is a bit like 'calculate', except you might be able to do the sum in your head.

Find...   You'll have to use a mixture of problem-solving skills and maths to find the answer to a question. It might not be immediately obvious what calculation you have to do.

Explain...   You have to use words to give reasons for something.

Show that...   You have to use maths to show that something is true.

> With 'explain' and 'show that' questions, the number of marks available can give you an idea of how much you need to write.

Functional Questions

> On Foundation Tier papers, 30-40% of the total marks available are from functional questions.

Some of the questions in your exams will be wordy questions about a real-life situation.
These are called functional questions. Functional questions are a bit trickier than normal questions because you have to work out what you are being asked to do. Here are some useful steps to follow:

1) Read the question carefully so you can work out what maths you need to use.
2) Underline the information that you need to answer the question
   — you won't always have to use all of the numbers they give you.
3) Write the question out in maths and then answer it, showing your working as usual.

In this book, questions which contain functional elements are marked with this stamp: | FUNCTIONAL |

Your exam paper won't mark them up though, so try to get used to how these questions look,
so that you can spot them in your exam.

Quality of Written Communication

> This may seem daft when it's a maths exam, but if the examiner doesn't think you've communicated your answer well enough, you'll lose marks.

In the exam, questions that have an asterisk (*) next to them are questions which test your quality of written communication. This means you'll be tested on your ability to explain things clearly, as well as your ability to do good maths. When you're answering questions like this, make sure you...

- Use your neatest handwriting so the examiner can easily read your answer.
- Check that your spelling, punctuation and grammar are ~~rigit rihgt~~ correct.
- Show every step of your working, and lay it out in a clear and coherent way.
- Use specialist wording if you need to.

(You should already be doing all these things in every answer anyway, so they're really nothing to worry about...)

Ordering Numbers and Place Value

1 Use the number lines to answer the following questions.

a) Write down the number shown by the arrow below. (G)

50 *1 2 3 4 5 6 7* 60   70

58

[1]

b) Write down the number shown by the arrow below. (G)

400   500   600   700

530

[1]

c) Find 2.6 on the number line below and mark it with an arrow (↑). (F)

2   3   4

[1]

[Total 3 marks]

2 Answer each of the following. (G)

a) Write 5079 in words.

Five thousand and seventy nine.

[1]

b) Write six thousand, one hundred and five as a number.

6105

[1]

c) What is the value of the figure 9 in 13 692?

90

[1]

[Total 3 marks]

3 Answer these questions. (G)

a) Write 26 004 in words.

Twenty six thousand and 4.

[1]

b) Write twenty thousand, three hundred and sixty-four as a number.

20864

[1]

c) What is the value of the figure 8 in 65 803?

802

[1]

[Total 3 marks]

4 Answer the following questions. (G)

a) Write 420 457 in words.

~~Four hundred and thousand four hundred and fifty Seven~~

[1]

b) Write six million as a number.

6,000 000

[1]

c) Write down the value of the figure 2 in 102 487

2 zero

[1]

[Total 3 marks]

5 The mileages of four cars are given below. Put the distances in order, starting with the lowest. (F)

98 653   100 003   98 649   100 010

98653 , 98649 , 100 003 , 10010.

[Total 1 mark]

6 Put these numbers in order of size, from high to low. (F)

53.3   35.6   35.54   52.91   35.06

58.3 , 52.91 , 35.6 , 35.54 , 35.06.

[Total 1 mark]

7 Anne has five cards, each with a number written on. (G)

| 4 | 7 | 1 | 8 | 2 |

She lines up all the cards to make a 5 digit number.

a) What is the smallest number she can make?

12478

[1]

b) What is the largest number she can make?

87421

[1]

[Total 2 marks]

Score:

16

Section One — Numbers

Addition and Subtraction

1   Work out 522 – 197.

$522 - 200 = 322 + 3 = 325$

....325....
[Total 2 marks]

FUNCTIONAL

2   Maci's car has failed its MOT. Using the information below, calculate the total cost of all the repairs.

MOT Results

FAIL

FAILED
Areas for attention:
- Exhaust — need full replacement
- Brakes — need new disc and pad on one wheel
- Tyres — tread depth too low on all tyres, need to replace all four

Price List	(includes labour costs and VAT)		
Tyres		**Exhaust**	
Each:	£28	Part Replacement:	£140
Pair:	£50	Full Replacement:	£290
Full Set:	£95		
		Maintenance	
Brakes		Oil Change:	£49
Pads (each):	£39	Adjust Tracking:	£62
Discs (each):	£59	AirCon Recharge:	£55
		Suspension Coil:	£98

£290
£98
£95

$193 + 90 = 283 + 200 = 483$

£ ....483....
[Total 3 marks]

3   Eric goes to town with £15. He spends £8.50 on a new scarf.
He meets his nan who gives him £20 and tells him to take £10 of it home for his sister.
Eric then sees a jumper he likes which costs £18.

If Eric buys the jumper, will he still have £10 to give to his sister? *No*
Show how you worked out your answer.

$£15 - 8.50 = £4.50$

$£24.50$

$-8 = £6.50$

Nob Bno for his sister

[Total 2 marks]

Section One — Numbers

4 Sue and Alan meet Mark in a juice bar. Mark offers to buy a round of drinks.

 Mark wants a Passion Fruit Punch and Sue and Alan both want a Tutti Frutti.

Mark pays with a £10 note. How much change will he get?

Juice Bar Price List	
St Clements:	£2.80
Cranberry Crush:	£2.90
Tutti Frutti:	£2.40
Passion Fruit Punch:	£2.15

£2.15
£4·80 } + = £6.95

£10 − 6.95 = £3.05

£ 3.05

[Total 2 marks]

5 Parvati and Zayn stop at a café for breakfast.

New Road Café			
Breakfast Snacks:		*Drinks:*	
Toast (2 slices)	£1.50	Tea	£1.40
Yoghurt with fruit	£1.90	Coffee	£1.50
Raisin bagel	£2.30	Fresh orange juice	£1.80
Breakfast deal of the day:			
Raisin bagel & fresh orange juice	£3.40		

Parvati has £3.30 and wants a breakfast snack and a hot drink.

a) List two combinations of snack and hot drink that she can get.

T T   Y T T C   T J   Y C

.....

[2]

Zayn buys 2 raisin bagels, a tea, a coffee and a fresh orange juice.
He pays the lowest possible price.

b) If he pays with a £10 note, how much change will he get?

Hint: don't forget the deal of the day.

£ .....

[3]

[Total 5 marks]

Score:

14

8

Multiplying and Dividing by 10, 100, etc.

1 Work out:

a) 32.8×10

328

[1]

b) $429 \div 10$

42.9

[1]

c) 22.2×1000 (F)

222 00

[1]

22.2 X10 222 00

[Total 3 marks]

2 Work out:

a) 4.268×100 (G)

[1]

b) $304 \div 100$ (G)

[1]

c) $2470 \div 1000$ (F)

[1]

[Total 3 marks]

3 Fill in the number missing from each box.

a) $23 \times$ $= 23\ 000$ (F)

1000

[1]

b) $46\ 000 \div$ $= 460$ (G)

1200

[1]

[Total 2 marks]

Score: ☐

8

 ☐   ☐   ☐

Multiplying and Dividing Without a Calculator

1 Work out 113×76

....

[Total 2 marks]

2 Work out:

   a) $19 + 26 \div 2$

....

[2]

b) $(22 - 18) \times (3 + 8)$

> Remember the rules for BODMAS.

....

[2]

[Total 4 marks]

3 $9 - 3 \times 2 + 2 = 14$ **D**

   Make this equation correct by writing it out with brackets.

....

[Total 1 mark]

FUNCTIONAL

4 Georgie is a sales representative. She drives to different companies to sell air conditioning units. **D**

   When she has to travel, her employer pays fuel expenses of 30p per mile. She drives to a job in the morning and drives home again later that day.
She is also given £8 to cover any food expenses for each day that she is not in the office.

The distances to her jobs for this week are shown on the right.

Find Georgie's total expenses for this week.

> Hint: think carefully about the total distance travelled.

This Week:

Mon — Buckshaw, 30 miles
Tues — in office
Weds — Wortham, 28 miles
Thurs — Harborough, 39 miles
Fri — Scotby, 40 miles

£ ....

[Total 5 marks]

Section One — Numbers

5   Alanna buys 15 tickets for a concert for her and some friends.
Each ticket is the same price. She pays with £200 and gets £5 change.

    How much does each ticket cost?

£ ....

[Total 3 marks]

FUNCTIONAL

6   James is having a party. He has worked out how much food he needs
to buy per person and goes to the shop to buy the things that he needs.

    Crisps come in 300 g packets.

There are 8 slices per pizza.

James is expecting there to be 15 people,
including himself, at the party.

> For each person:
> * 3 slices of pizza
> * 25 g of crisps

How many pizzas and how many packets of crisps does he need to buy?

.... pizzas

.... packets of crisps

[Total 5 marks]

FUNCTIONAL

*7   The charges for Sharon's monthly water bill are shown below.

Water Bill Charges	
Fixed Monthly payment	**£7**
Fresh water	**12p** per 100 litres
Waste water disposal	**9p** per 100 litres

This month, Sharon's family used 9300 litres of fresh water
and disposed of 8600 litres of waste water.
Calculate how much Sharon's water bill will be this month.

£ ....

[Total 6 marks]

Exam Practice Tip

It's always important to show your working, but it's especially important for these non-calculator questions — because they all include marks for using a correct method. If you don't show your working, you'll be throwing away valuable marks in the exam.

Score

26

Multiplying and Dividing with Decimals

1 Give your answers to the following, without using a calculator:

 a) 16×0.7

~~~~ Hint: try working out 16 × 7 first. ~~~~

16 × 7 = 112   11.2

..........11.2..........
[2]

b) 2.5×1.9

25×19

$25 \times 1 \text{v} = 23, \times 2 = 500 - 23 = 475$

.........4.75.........
[2]

[Total 4 marks]

2 Given that $56 \times 427 = 23\,912$, find the value of:

 a) 5.6×4.27

....
[1]

b) $0.56 \times 4\,270\,000$

....
[1]

c) $2391.2 \div 4.27$

....
[1]

[Total 3 marks]

3 Work out 0.7×0.8

 0.056

...........0.056...........
[Total 2 marks]

4 Work out the value of each of the following:

 a) $14 \div 0.7$

$$14 \div 0.7 = \frac{14}{0.7} = \frac{\text{.......}}{7} = \text{.......}$$

....
[2]

b) $23 \div 0.46$

$\dfrac{23}{46} = 0.5$

....
[2]

[Total 4 marks]

Score:

13

Negative Numbers

1   Put the numbers below in order from lowest to highest.

    −102.4   98.9   −102.7   99.5   −99.8   −98.9   −103.1

    .... , ... , ... , ... , ... , ... , ...

    [Total 1 mark]

2   The table below shows the minimum and maximum
    temperatures in four cities one day in January.

City	Min. temperature (°C)	Max. temperature (°C)
London	4	9
Paris	7	11
St Petersburg	−8	−2
Christchurch	16	22

a) What was the difference between the maximum and minimum temperatures in London?

                                                        .... °C
                                                              [1]

b) Which city had the **lowest** minimum temperature?

                                                ....
                                                              [1]

c) What was the difference in temperature between the highest maximum
   temperature and the lowest minimum temperature across the four cities?

                                                        .... °C
                                                              [3]

                                                        [Total 5 marks]

3   Work out:

    a) -11×7

                    -77

                                                        ....
                                                              [1]

    b) $-72 \div -8$

                                                        ....
                                                              [1]

                    -8

                                                        [Total 2 marks]

                                                        Score:

                                                          8

Special Types of Number

1 Choose a number from the list which matches each description.

12   100   32   41   27   15   50

a) An odd number bigger than 30. **(F)**

................41..........

[1]

b) A square number. **(F)**

................100..........

[1]

c) A cube number. **(E)**

................27..........

[1]

[Total 3 marks]

2 Write down the value of each of the following:

 a) 9^2 **(F)**

................81..........

[1]

b) 4^3 **(E)**

................64..........

[1]

c) $\sqrt{36}$ **(F)**

................6..........

[1]

[Total 3 marks]

Score:

6

Section One — Numbers

Prime Numbers, Multiples and Factors

1 Look at the list of numbers below.

> 1   7   11   12   15   21

a) Write down a number from the list which is a prime number.

....
[1]

b) Which number in the list is a multiple of 5?

....
[1]

c) Write down a number from the list which is a factor of 30 and is greater than 5.

....
[1]

d) Write down two numbers from the list whose sum is a prime number.

.... and ....
[1]

[Total 4 marks]

2 Write down:

a) **all** the factors of 20,

....
[2]

b) all the multiples of 8 which appear in the list below.

> 55 56 57 58   59 60 61 62 63 64 65

....
[1]

[Total 3 marks]

3 Write down:

a) two multiples of 21,

.... , ...
[1]

b) a prime number between 45 and 50.

....
[1]

[Total 2 marks]

Score:

9

Prime Factors, LCM and HCF

1 Find:

a) 72 as a product of its prime factors.

> Make sure your answer only uses prime numbers.
> Multiply them all together to check you get the
> number you started with.

$72 = 2 \times \ldots \times \ldots \times \ldots \times \ldots$

....

[2]

b) the highest common factor (HCF) of 54 and 72.

....

[1]

[Total 3 marks]

2 Two remote-control cars start at the same time from the start line on a track.

One car takes 3 minutes to complete a circuit.
The other car takes 5 minutes to complete a circuit.

If they start side by side, how long will it be before they are next
side by side at the start line?

$$3 \qquad 5$$
$$6 \qquad 10$$
$$9 \qquad 15$$

.... minutes
[Total 2 marks]

FUNCTIONAL

3 Phil is making jam.

He needs to buy mini jam jars which come in packs of 35 and lids which
come in packs of 55. He doesn't want to have any jars or lids left over.

What is the minimum number of packs of jars he needs to buy?

Multiples of 35 are: 35, 70, ..., ..., ..., ..., ..., ..., ..., ..., ..., ...
Multiples of 55 are: 55, 110, ..., ..., ..., ..., ..., ...

So the LCM is ...., which is the minimum number of jars he needs.
So the minimum number of packs he needs is .... ÷ .... = ... packs

....
[Total 3 marks]

Score: ☐

8

 ☐   ☐   ☐

Section One — Numbers

Fractions, Decimals and Percentages

1 Convert each of the following: (E)

a) $\frac{3}{4}$ to a decimal.

....
[1]

b) 0.06 to a percentage.

....
[1]

c) 35% to a fraction in its simplest form.

....
[2]

[Total 4 marks]

2 Mary and Sam both sat a maths test and were given a mark out of 20. (E)

Mary scored $\frac{14}{20}$.

a) Convert her score to a percentage.

.... %
[2]

Sam got 85% on the test.

b) What was Sam's mark out of 20 as a fraction?

....
[2]

[Total 4 marks]

3 Write $\frac{3}{5}$, 80% and 0.65 in order from smallest to largest. (E)

.... , ..., ...
[Total 2 marks]

Score: ⬚
10

Equivalent Fractions

1 Answer the following questions.

 a) Write the fraction $\frac{12}{30}$ in its simplest form.

handwritten: $\frac{6}{15}$ $\frac{2}{5}$

answer: $\frac{2}{5}$

[1]

b) Find the fraction of the shape below which is shaded.
Write this fraction in its simplest form.

....

[2]

c) Shade $\frac{4}{5}$ of the shape to the right. *(handwritten: 50)*

[1]

[Total 4 marks]

2 Convert each of the following:

 a) $\frac{18}{7}$ to a mixed number.

....

[1]

b) $1\frac{3}{4}$ to an improper fraction.

....

[1]

[Total 2 marks]

3 Use the lists of fractions below to answer the following questions.

 a) Give the **two** fractions from the list below that are not equivalent to $\frac{1}{3}$

$\frac{3}{9}$ $=\frac{1}{3}$ $\frac{2}{6}$ $=\frac{1}{3}$ $\frac{3}{12}$ $\frac{5}{15}$ $\frac{1}{3}$ $\frac{6}{20}$ $\frac{3}{10}$ $\frac{8}{24}$

answer: $\frac{3}{12}$ $\frac{6}{20}$

[2]

b) Which fraction in the following list is the largest?

$\frac{4}{5}$ $\frac{25}{20}$ $\frac{7}{9}$ $\frac{13}{15}$ $=$

You must show your working.

$\frac{4}{5}=\frac{......}{45}$ $\frac{7}{9}=\frac{......}{......}$ $\frac{13}{15}=\frac{......}{......}$

....

[3]

[Total 5 marks]

Score:

11

Fractions

1 Work out the following:

 a) $\frac{1}{2} \times \frac{1}{6}$ $\qquad \frac{1}{2} \times \frac{1}{6} = \frac{..... \times .....}{..... \times .....} = \frac{.....}{.....}$

....

[1]

b) $\frac{2}{3} \div \frac{3}{5}$ $\qquad \frac{2}{3} \div \frac{3}{5} = \frac{2}{3} \times \frac{.....}{.....} = \frac{..... \times .....}{..... \times .....} = \frac{.....}{.....}$

....

[2]

[Total 3 marks]

2 Find the following:

 a) $\frac{3}{4} \times \frac{2}{5}$, giving your answer in its simplest form.

....

[2]

b) $\frac{2}{9}$ as a decimal.

$$9\overline{)2.000...}$$

....

[3]

[Total 5 marks]

3 Find the following:

 a) $\frac{1}{6} + \frac{2}{3}$ $\qquad \frac{1}{6} + \frac{2}{3} = \frac{1}{6} + \frac{.....}{6} = \frac{..... + ...}{.....} = \frac{.....}{.....}$

....

[2]

b) $\frac{7}{8} - \frac{3}{4}$ $\qquad \frac{7}{8} - \frac{3}{4} = \frac{7}{8} - \frac{.....}{8} = \frac{..... - .....}{.....} = \frac{.....}{.....}$

....

[2]

[Total 4 marks]

4 Work out the following. Write your answers in their simplest form. **D**

a) $\frac{1}{3} + \frac{2}{5}$ Make sure each fraction has the same denominator before you try to add them.

....

[2]

b) $\frac{1}{2} - \frac{2}{7}$

....

[2]

[Total 4 marks]

5 Find:

 a) $\frac{3}{5}$ of 60.

$60\%5 = 12 \times 3 = £36$

...........36...........

[2]

b) 15 out of 40 as a fraction in its simplest form.

$\frac{15}{40} = \frac{3}{8}$

...........3/8...........

[2]

[Total 4 marks]

6 The turnout at last Saturday's Norchester City game was 12 400.
Season ticket holders made up $\frac{3}{8}$ of the crowd.
How many season ticket holders were there?

$12400 \% 8 = 1550 \times 3 = 4650$

...........4650...........

[Total 2 marks]

7 A school library has £79 to spend on books.
They must spend $\frac{7}{10}$ of the money on non-fiction books and the rest on fiction.

How much must they spend on fiction books?

$79 / 10 = 7.9 \times 7 = 55.3$

£ ....55.3...........

[Total 3 marks]

8 Sarah is ordering pizza for her birthday party.

 There will be 12 people in total at her party.
Sarah wants to order enough so that each person can have $\frac{2}{5}$ of a pizza.
How many pizzas should she order?

....

[Total 3 marks]

Section One — Numbers

FUNCTIONAL

*9   Chris is buying a car. The car dealer offers him two different ways to pay.

Full price:
£1100

Pay in full today and get $\frac{1}{4}$ off the full price.

Pay £150 today, then pay 12 monthly payments of £55.

Which is the cheaper way for Chris to pay for the car?
You must show your working.

1100 − 150 = 950   12×55 = 660

[Total 4 marks]

10   Write down the reciprocal of $\frac{1}{7}$

....

[Total 1 mark]

11    $\frac{1}{11}$ can be written as the recurring decimal, 0.09090909...

    Write 0.09090909... in recurring decimal form.

....

[Total 1 mark]

12   Here is a list of fractions: $\frac{1}{4}, \frac{1}{5}, \frac{1}{7}, \frac{1}{8}$

    Which of these fractions can be written as a recurring decimal?

....

[Total 1 mark]

Score: ☐

35

Section One — Numbers   ☐   ☐   ☐

Proportion Problems

1 Brown sauce can be bought in three different sizes. The price of each is shown on the right. Which size of bottle is the best value for money?

250 ml £2.30   330 ml £2.97   500 ml £4.10

$250 \% 2.30 = 1.68$

$330 \% 297 = 1.11$

$500 \% 410 = 1.21$

..........250.......... ml

[Total 2 marks]

2 Cat is baking some muffins for an event in her village hall. The list of ingredients below will make 20 muffins.

```
            Ingredients
175 g flour (plain)
175 g butter
120 g sugar
2½ tsp baking powder
4 eggs (medium)
```

Cat wants to make enough muffins for 70 people.

Work out how much she will need of each ingredient.

Flour: (175 ÷ 20) × 70 = ... g

Butter: (............ ÷ 20) × 70 = ... g

Sugar: (............ ÷ ....) × .... = ... g

Baking powder: (............ ÷ ....) × .... = ... tsp

Eggs: (............ ÷ ....) × .... = ...

Flour: .... g

Butter: .... g

Sugar: .... g

Baking powder: .... tsp

Eggs: ....

[Total 3 marks]

Exam Practice Tip

Proportion is really just all about multiplying and dividing — in general, it's quite likely that you can answer questions on proportion (like the ones on this page) by finding the amount/cost for "one thing" and then either using this to compare the different options, or multiplying it by the number of things you need.

Score

5

Percentages

1   Find 60% of £450.

£ ....

[Total 2 marks]

2   A farmer has 50 pigs. 35 of the pigs are female.

What percentage of the pigs are male?

....

[Total 3 marks]

3   Aled wants to buy a suitcase to take on holiday.

He sees a suitcase which was £18, but today it has 10% off.

a) How much money would he get off the suitcase if he bought it today?

£ ....

[2]

He sees another suitcase which was £24, but the ticket says today the price is reduced by £6.

b) What is £6 as a percentage of £24?

.... %

[2]

[Total 4 marks]

4   Jane owns a fashion shop. She sells a pair of jeans for £33.25 plus VAT at 20%.

How much does she sell the pair of jeans for?

£ ....

[Total 3 marks]

Exam Practice Tip

There are two key things to remember for percentage questions in the exam. To find a percentage of an amount, turn the percentage into a decimal (by dividing by 100), then multiply this by the amount.
To find one amount as a percentage of another, divide the first amount by the second, then multiply by 100.

Score

12

Ratios

1   Give the ratio 4 : 12 in its simplest form.

....

[Total 1 mark]

2   In a class of 26 children, 12 are boys and 14 are girls.

     a) What is the ratio of boys to girls? Give your answer in its simplest form.

....

[1]

     b) In another class, the ratio of boys to girls is 2 : 3. There are 25 children in the class. How many girls are there?

....

[2]

[Total 3 marks]

FUNCTIONAL

3   Brian is making a fruit punch. He mixes orange juice, pineapple juice and lemonade in the ratio 4 : 3 : 7. He makes 700 ml of fruit punch.

     What volume of each drink does he use?

Hint: start by trying to find the volume of one "part".

     1 part = 700 ÷ (......... + ... + ...)

           = 700 ÷ ....

           = ... ml

     Orange juice: .... × 4 = ... ml
     Pineapple juice: .... × .... = ... ml
     Lemonade: .... × .... = ... ml

Orange juice: .... ml

Pineapple juice: .... ml

Lemonade: .... ml

[Total 3 marks]

Section One — Numbers

4 Andy, Louise and Christine have £160. They share it in the ratio 3 : 6 : 7. **(D)**

How much money did Christine get?

£ ....
[Total 2 marks]

5 Fran and Rob both sell some raffle tickets. The ratio of the number of tickets Fran **(D)** sells to the number of tickets Rob sells is 9 : 7. Fran sells 360 tickets.

How many tickets did they sell altogether?

....
[Total 3 marks]

6 Farmer Joe is planting his orchard with apple trees and cherry trees. **(D)** The ratio of apple trees to cherry trees is 4 : 5.

a) Hannah says that this means Farmer Joe's orchard must contain 4 apple trees and 5 cherry trees. Explain why Hannah may be wrong.

....
[1]

b) Farmer Joe plants 126 trees in total. How many of each type of tree are there?

Apple ....

Cherry ....
[3]

[Total 4 marks]

Score:

16

Rounding Off and Estimating Calculations

1   Round the following to the given degree of accuracy.

a) Josh has 123 people coming to his party. **(F)**
Write this number to the nearest 10.

....
[1]

b) The attendance at a football match was 2568 people. **(F)**
What is this to the nearest hundred?

....
[1]

c) The population of Ulverpool is 452 529. **(E)**
Round this to the nearest 100 000.

....
[1]

d) The distance between two stars is 428.6237 light years. **(E)**
Round this distance to one decimal place.

.... light years
[1]

[Total 4 marks]

2   Use your calculator to find: **(D)**

$$\frac{4.32^2 - \sqrt{13.4}}{16.3 + 2.19}$$

Give your answer to 3 significant figures.

....
[Total 2 marks]

3   Answer the following: **(C)**

a) Estimate the value of $\dfrac{3.2 \times 398.4}{1.87^2}$

> You should start by rounding each number to an easier one.

....
[2]

b) Mr Potts is trying to work out the cost of his electricity bill.
He has used 1720 units. He estimates it will cost £100.
Is Mr Potts correct? Show all your working.

Energy Save
Fixed price electricity 11.3p per unit

[3]
[Total 5 marks]

Score: ☐

11

Powers and Roots

1   Use your calculator to find the following:

a) 8.7^3

....

[1]

b) $\sqrt{2025}$

....

[1]

[Total 2 marks]

2   Estimate the value of $\sqrt{42}$ (F)

....

[Total 1 mark]

3   Write as a single power of 6: (C)

a) $6^4 \times 6^7$

....

[1]

b) $\dfrac{6^5}{6^3}$

....

[1]

[Total 2 marks]

4   Simplify the expression $\dfrac{3^4 \times 3^7}{3^6}$. Leave your answer in index form. (C)

....

[Total 2 marks]

Score: ☐

7

Section One — Numbers

Simplifying Terms

1 Simplify the following.

a) $p + p + p + p$

....

[1]

b) $m + 3m - 2m$

....

[1]

c) $7r - 2p - 4r + 6p$

....

[2]

[Total 4 marks]

2 Simplify the following.

a) $w \times w \times w \times w \times w$ **D**

....

[1]

b) $x^9 \div x^3$ **C**

....

[1]

c) $y^2 \times y^3$ **C**

....

[1]

[Total 3 marks]

3 Write the following in their simplest form. **D**

a) $2a \times 5b$

....

[1]

b) $5pq + pq - 2pq$

....

[1]

c) $2x^2 + 8x - 4x - x^2$

....

[2]

[Total 4 marks]

Score:

11

Multiplying Out Brackets

1 Expand the following.

a) $3(x - 2)$

$= (3 \times \text{............}) + (3 \times \text{............}) = \text{............} - \text{............}$

....
[1]

b) $x(x + 4)$

....
[1]

[Total 2 marks]

2 Multiply out the brackets and simplify where possible.

a) $5(x + y)$

....
[1]

b) $s(2s - 3)$

....
[1]

c) $2a(2a + 3)$

$= (2a \times \text{............}) + (2a \times \text{............}) = \text{............} + \text{............}$

....
[1]

d) $2b - 3(b - 1)$

....
[2]

[Total 5 marks]

FOIL

3 Expand and simplify where possible.

a) $3(x - 1) + 5(x + 2)$

$3x - 3$ $5x + 10$ $8x + 7$

.......$8x + 7$.......
[2]

b) $4a(a + 2b)$

$4a^2 + 8ab$

....
[1]

c) $9 - 3(x + 2)$

....
[2]

[Total 5 marks]

Score:

12

Section Two — Algebra

Taking Out Common Factors

1 Factorise the following expressions.

a) $6x + 3$

$2x + 1$

$2x + 3$

[1]

b) $x^2 + 7x$

....
[1]

c) $25p - 15q$

....
[1]

[Total 3 marks]

2 Factorise fully $4a^2 - 24ab$.

$$4a^2 - 24ab = 4(\text{............} - \text{............})$$
$$= 4\text{......}(\text{............} - \text{............})$$

....
[Total 2 marks]

3 Factorise the following expressions fully.

a) $7y - 21y^2$

....
[2]

b) $18t + 9t^2$

....
[2]

[Total 4 marks]

4 Factorise these expressions fully.

a) $4x^2 + 6xy$

....
[2]

b) $2vw + 8v^2$

....
[2]

[Total 4 marks]

Exam Practice Tip

In the exam, you can check that you've factorised an expression properly by expanding the brackets back out. You should get the same expression that you started with. If you don't then something must have gone wrong somewhere down the line and you'll need to give it another go. Sorry about that.

Score

13

Solving Equations

1 Solve these equations for x.

a) $x + 3 = 12$

$x = $ ....

[1]

b) $6x = 24$

$x = $ ....

[1]

[Total 2 marks]

2 Solve the equations below.

 a) $p - 11 = -7$

$p = $ ....

[1]

b) $2y - 5 = 9$

$y = $ ....

[2]

c) $3z + 2 = z + 15$

$3z - z = 15 - $ ....

$2z = $ ....

$z = $ .... ÷ .... = ...

$z = $ ....

[2]

[Total 5 marks]

3 Solve these equations for x.

 a) $3x + 5 = 14$

$x = $ ....

[2]

b) $7x - 4 = 2x + 1$

$x = $ ....

[2]

[Total 4 marks]

4 Solve the following equations.

a) $40 - 3x = 17x$

$x =$ ....

[2]

b) $2y - 5 = 3y - 12$

$y =$ ....

[2]

[Total 4 marks]

5 Find the solution to each of the following equations.

 a) $3(a + 2) = 15$

$(3 \times \text{.........}) + (3 \times \text{.........}) = 15$

$\text{.........} + \text{.........} = 15$

$\text{.........} = \text{.........}$

$a = \text{.........}$

$a =$ ....

[3]

b) $2b - 6 = 2(3b + 1)$

$b =$ ....

[3]

[Total 6 marks]

6 Solve the following equations.

 a) $9(e - 2) = 3e + 6$

$e =$ ....

[3]

b) $5(2c - 1) = 4(3c - 2)$

$c =$ ....

[3]

[Total 6 marks]

Exam Practice Tip

It's a good idea to check your solution by substituting it back into the equation and checking that everything works out properly. It certainly beats sitting and twiddling your thumbs or counting sheep for the last few minutes of your exam.

Score

27

Writing Equations

1 Alexa is playing a number game.

Alexa thinks of a number and multiplies it by 7. She subtracts 12 from this new number.
Her answer is equal to 4 times her original number.

What was her original number?

$x \times 7 - 12$

Answer 4 $4 \times 7 = 28 - 12 = 16$ 4

[Total 2 marks]

2 ABC is an equilateral triangle and EFGH is a rectangle.
ABC and EFGH have the same perimeter.

Remember that all the sides of an equilateral triangle are the same length.

Diagram not drawn to scale

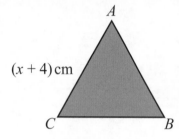

$(x + 4)\,\text{cm}$

$(2x + 4)\,\text{cm}$

$(x - 1)\,\text{cm}$

Find the value of x. Show all your working.

Perimeter of ABC = perimeter of EFGH

$3(x + 4) = 2(2x + 4) +$ ....

$(3 \times \text{..........}) + (3 \times \text{..........}) = (2 \times 2x) + (2 \times 4) + \text{..........} + \text{..........}$

$\text{..........} + \text{..........} = 4x + 8 + \text{..........} - \text{..........}$

$\text{..........}x + \text{..........} = \text{..........}x + \text{..........}$

$\text{..........}x = \text{..........}$

$x = \text{..........}$

$x = \text{..................................}$

[Total 4 marks]

3 ABC is a triangle.

Find the size of the largest angle.
Make sure you show all your working.

Angles in a triangle add up to 180°.

Diagram not drawn to scale

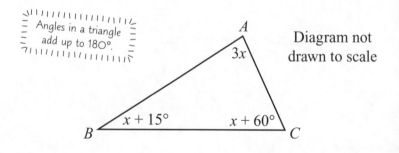

$3x$

$x + 15°$

$x + 60°$

.................................°

[Total 4 marks]

Score:

10

Using Formulas

1 $Q = 7x - 3y$

 Find the value of Q when $x = 8$ and $y = 7$.

....

[Total 2 marks]

2 $S = 4m^2 + 2.5n$

Calculate the value of S when $m = 6.5$ and $n = 4$.

S = (4 × .... × ....) + (2.5 × ....)

S = ... + ...

S = ...

....

[Total 2 marks]

3   The formula for converting a temperature in Celsius (C) to a temperature in Fahrenheit (F) is:

$$F = \frac{9C}{5} + 32$$

Convert 35 °C to Fahrenheit.

.... °F

[Total 2 marks]

4   The cost of hiring a bouncy castle is calculated using the formula below.

$$C = S + 7H$$

C is the cost in £, S is the charge in £ to set the castle up and H is the number of hours it is hired for.

a) How much will it cost to hire a bouncy castle for 13 hours if the set-up charge is £25?

£ ....

[2]

b) The cost of hiring a set of space hoppers is calculated using a different formula:

$$C = 2H + 5N$$

C is the cost in £, H is the number of hours the space hoppers are hired for, and N is the number of space hoppers hired. How much would it cost to hire 5 space hoppers for 3 hours?

£ ....

[2]

[Total 4 marks]

Score:

10

Section Two — Algebra

Writing and Rearranging Formulas

1 To hire a cement mixer, Alex pays £50 per day plus a flat fee of £300. (E)

a) Write a formula to show the total cost C (in £) of hiring the cement mixer for d days.

Total cost = flat fee + (cost per day × number of days)
C = ... + (.................. × ....)
C = ... + ...

....
[2]

b) How much would Alex have to pay to hire the cement mixer for 3 days?

£.............................
[2]

[Total 4 marks]

2 To convert kilometres into miles, Tasmin says that you divide (E) the number of kilometres by 8 and multiply the answer by 5.

a) Write this rule as a formula.
Use k to represent the number of kilometres and m to represent the number of miles.

....
[2]

b) Use your formula to convert 110 kilometres into miles.

.... miles
[2]

[Total 4 marks]

3 Len and Sam have been shopping for books. (E)

a) Len spent m pounds more than Sam.
If Sam spent v pounds, write an expression to show how much Len spent.

....
[1]

b) Each page of one of the books is 0.1 mm thick.
The front and back covers are both 3 mm thick.
Write a formula to show the total thickness t (in mm) of a book with x pages.

....
[2]

[Total 3 marks]

4 A furniture delivery company charges a flat fee of £35 per delivery, plus an additional £10 for each piece of furniture.

a) Write a formula giving the total cost A (in £) of a delivery of F pieces of furniture. (E)

....

[2]

b) Atish is charged £105 for the delivery of some furniture to his new house. (D)
How many pieces of furniture is he having delivered?

....

[3]

[Total 5 marks]

5 Shape **M** is shown below. P is the perimeter of shape **M**. (E)

> The perimeter is the distance around the edge of a shape.

Write a formula for P in terms of x.

$2x$ $2x$

$2x + 1$

$2x + 1$

$3x - 5$

$4x + 3$

Diagram not drawn to scale

....

[Total 3 marks]

6 The formula $v = u + at$ can be used to calculate the speed of a car. (C)

a) Rearrange the formula to make u the subject.

....

[1]

b) Rearrange the formula to make t the subject.

....

[2]

[Total 3 marks]

Exam Practice Tip

Remember that a <u>formula</u> is just like an equation — it has an equals sign in it, like 'P = 2x + 3'. An <u>expression</u> doesn't have an equals sign — it's just something like '2x + 3'. If you're asked to give a formula in the exam, make sure you give the whole thing and not just an expression, otherwise you won't get all the marks.

Score

22

Section Two — Algebra

Number Patterns and Sequences

1 Here are the first four terms of a sequence. (E)

      4   12   20   28

a) Write down the next two terms in the sequence.

.... and ....

[1]

b) The 25th term in the sequence is 196. Write down the 23rd term in the sequence.

....

[1]

c) Thomas says that the 12th term is 90. Explain why he is incorrect.

....

....

[2]

[Total 4 marks]

2 Fill in the gaps in the following sequences, and give the rule for each sequence. (E)

a)   13   18   23   33   ....

Rule: ....

[2]

b)   6   12   24   48   ....

Rule: ....

[2]

[Total 4 marks]

3 A sequence is made from patterns of triangles. The first three patterns are shown below. (E)

a) Draw the fourth pattern in the sequence.

[1]

b) How many small triangles are there in the ninth pattern in the sequence?
Give a reason for your answer.

....

[2]

[Total 3 marks]

4 The *n*th term of a sequence is $n^2 + 4$.

a) Find the first term of the sequence.

....
[1]

b) Find the 8th term of the sequence.

....
[1]

[Total 2 marks]

5 The first four terms in a sequence are 2, 9, 16, 23, ...

a) Find the *n*th term of the sequence.

2   9   16   23

The common difference is ...., so ....n is in the formula.

....

n = 1   2   ....

........n = ...

↓   ↓   ↓   ↓   You have to subtract .... to get to the term.

nth term = ...

So the expression for the nth term is ....n − ....

....
[2]

b) What is the 30th term of the sequence?

....
[1]

[Total 3 marks]

6 This question is about the sequence 3, 7, 11, 15, 19...

Find the *n*th term of the sequence.

$1 \times 4 - 1 = 3$

$2 \times 4 - 1 = \cancel{8}7$

$4n - 1$

....
[Total 2 marks]

Score: [ ]

18

Section Two — Algebra

Trial and Improvement

1   Use trial and improvement to find the solution of the equation $x^3 + 4x = 24$.

Give your answer correct to 1 decimal place and show all your working.

x	$x^3 + 4x$	
2	$2^3 + (4 \times 2) = 8 + 8 = 16$	Too small
3	$3^3 + (4 \times 3) =$ .... + ... = ...	....

$x =$ ....

[Total 4 marks]

2   Find the solution of the equation $x^3 - 2x = 0$ correct to 1 decimal place.

Use the trial and improvement method and show your working.

$x =$ ....

[Total 4 marks]

Exam Practice Tip

Make sure that you learn the method for solving trial and improvement problems — don't go randomly plugging in numbers all over the place. It's really important that you show all your working — the examiner needs to see that you've been systematic and tried all the values you're supposed to have done.

Score

8

Section Two — Algebra

Inequalities

1 Write down the inequality shown on the number line below.

inequality $x \geqslant -2$

[Total 1 mark]

2 n is an integer. List all the possible values of n that satisfy the inequality $-3 \leq n < 2$.

....

[Total 2 marks]

3 $2a - 7 \leq 11$

a) Solve this inequality.

....

[2]

b) Indicate the solution to this inequality on the number line below.

[2]

[Total 4 marks]

4 Solve the following inequalities.

a) $2p > 4$

....

[1]

b) $4q - 5 < 23$

....

[2]

c) $4r - 2 \geq 2r + 5$

....

[2]

[Total 5 marks]

Score:

12

Coordinates and Midpoints

1   Two points have been plotted on the grid below. They are labelled **A** and **B**.

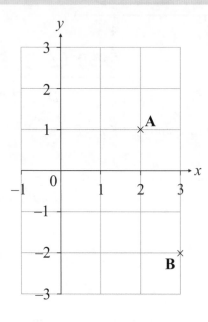

a) Give the coordinates of point **A**.

(......2...., ...1......)

[1]

b) Give the coordinates of point **B**.

(..............., ...2.......)

[1]

c) Point **C** has the coordinates (1, −1).
Mark this point on the grid on the left using a cross (×) and label it **C**.

[1]

[Total 3 marks]

2   Points **Q** and **R** have been plotted on the grid below.

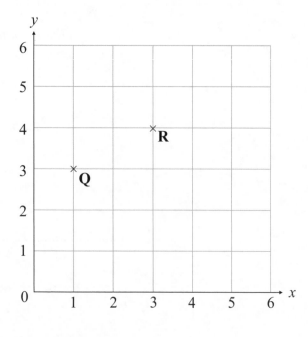

a) What are the coordinates of point **Q**?

(..............., ...)

[1]

b) Point **S** lies on the *x*-axis.
The line **QS** is parallel to the *y*-axis.
What are the coordinates of point **S**?

(..............., ...)

[2]

c) Point **T** lies on the *y*-axis.
The line **TR** is parallel to the *x*-axis.
What are the coordinates of point **T**?

(..............., ...)

[2]

[Total 5 marks]

3 Points **A** and **B** have been plotted on the grid below:

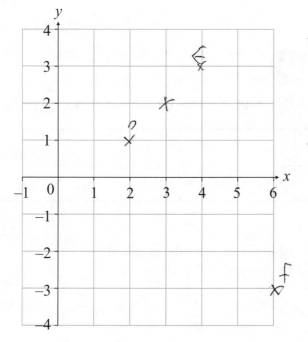

a) Write down the coordinates of the midpoint of the line segment **AB**.

$$\left(\frac{1 + \ldots}{2}, \frac{\ldots + \ldots}{\ldots}\right) = (\ldots, \ldots)$$

(.............., ...)

[2]

b) Point **C** has the coordinates (1, –3).
Basil thinks the midpoint of the line segment **BC** is at (2, –1).
Explain why he is wrong.

....

[1]

[Total 3 marks]

4 A grid has been drawn below.

a) Plot the points **D** (2, 1), **E** (4, 3) and **F** (6, –3) on this grid.

[1]

b) Find the midpoint of the line segment **DE**.

(....3...., ...2....)

[2]

c) Find the midpoint of the line segment **DF**.

(....4...., ...–1....)

[2]

[Total 5 marks]

Score:

16

Section Three — Graphs

Straight-Line Graphs

1 Answer each question below.

 a) Complete this table of values for the equation $y = 3x - 2$.

x	-2	-1	0	1	2
y		-5			

[2]

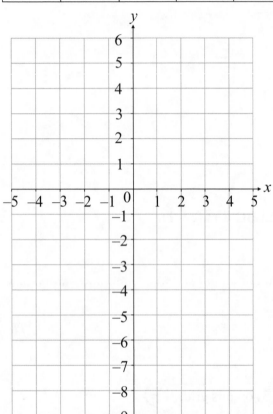

b) Use your table of values to plot the graph of $y = 3x - 2$ on the grid.

[2]

c) On the same grid, plot the graph of $y = -2x + 2$ from $x = -2$ to $x = 2$.

In the exam, you might not always be given a table of values to help you plot a graph — but it's a good idea to draw your own.

[3]

[Total 7 marks]

2 This is a question about the equation $y + 3x = 8$

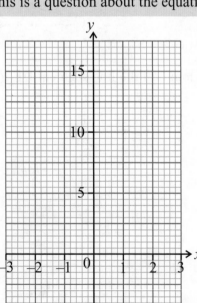

a) Complete this table of values for the equation $y + 3x = 8$.

x	-2	-1	0	1	2
y				5	

[2]

b) Using the table above, draw the graph of $y + 3x = 8$ on the grid to the left.

[2]

[Total 4 marks]

Section Three — Graphs

3   Use the grid for the questions below.

    a) Draw the graph of $y = 2x - 2$
       for values of x from -1 to 3.

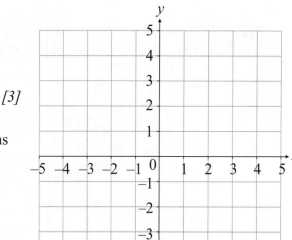

                                             [3]

     b) Draw the graph of $y = 4$.
         Use this to solve the simultaneous equations
              $y = 2x - 2$
              $y = 4$

Look at the point where the lines cross.

                            $x = $ ....,

                            $y = $ ....
                                [3]

                     [Total 6 marks]

4   The equation of a graph is $y = 3x + 8$.

Write down the gradient of this line.

                                      ....

                                 [Total 1 mark]

5   Below are the equations of five graphs.

     $y = 3x$ $y = 2x + 6$ $y = x + 6$ $y = 4x - 1$ $y = \frac{1}{2}x + 3$

a) Write down the equation of the steepest graph.

                                      ....

                                 [1]

b) Amie says, "the graphs $y = 2x + 6$ and $y = x + 6$ will be parallel to each other".
    Is she correct? Give a reason for your answer.

....

....

                                 [1]

                     [Total 2 marks]

Exam Practice Tip

When you're drawing straight-line graphs, make sure you always use a ruler — otherwise you'll be throwing away valuable marks in the exam. If one of your points doesn't fit in a straight line with the others, the chances are you've made a mistake filling in your table of values — so it's best to go back and double-check.

Score

20

Travel Graphs

1 The travel graph below shows Selby's bike ride from his house (**A**) to the zoo (**C**), which is 25 km away.

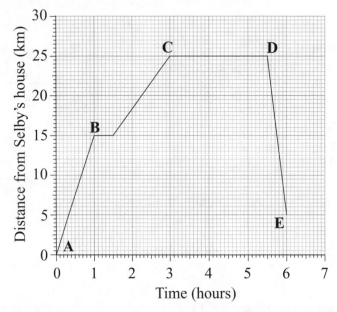

a) After one hour, Selby stops at a bench (**B**) for a rest.
Find the gradient of the line between point **A** and point **B**.

$$\frac{15 - 0}{\ldots - \ldots} = \frac{\ldots}{\ldots} = \ldots$$

....

[2]

b) What does the gradient of the line between point **A** and point **B** represent?

....

[1]

c) How long was Selby's journey to the zoo (**C**) from home (**A**)?

.... hours

[1]

d) How long did Selby spend at the zoo?

.... hours

[1]

e) After the zoo, Selby stopped at the shops (**E**) for 30 minutes before cycling straight home at a constant speed. Given that he arrived home 7 hours after he had first left, complete the graph above.

[2]

f) How many hours did Selby spend cycling in total during the day?

.... hours

[1]

[Total 8 marks]

2 Marcus lives in Barcastle, 90 miles away from Appleborough.

At 12 o'clock midday Marcus left his home and travelled to Appleborough.
The graph below shows his journey to Appleborough.

a) How long did he take to complete the first 40 miles?

.... hours

[1]

b) Marcus stayed in Appleborough for 45 minutes.
He then travelled straight home at a speed of 45 mph.
Complete the travel graph.

Remember: speed = distance ÷ time

[2]

c) How long does Marcus spend away
from home in total throughout the day?

.... hours .... minutes

[1]

d) Between which times is Marcus
travelling the fastest?

.... pm and .... pm

[1]

[Total 5 marks]

3 Katherine is going to the cinema.

She leaves her house at 1 pm and walks at a constant speed of 3.5 mph.
Katherine arrives at the cinema 2 hours later.
She stays for 3 hours and 45 minutes, and then travels straight home by bus.

a) Given that Katherine arrives back home
at 7 pm, use the grid on the left to draw a
distance-time graph showing her journey.

[3]

b) What is Katherine's average speed on the
bus home?

.... mph

[2]

[Total 5 marks]

Score: ☐

18

Section Three — Graphs

Conversion Graphs

1   Use the graph to help you answer the questions below.

a) A petrol tank holds 8 gallons.
How many litres is this?

.... litres
[1]

b) Approximately how many gallons of water
would fit into a 20 litre container?

.... gallons
[1]

c) A paddling pool holds 80 litres of water. What is this in gallons?

40 litres = ... gallons

40 × .... = 80,

so, ... gallons × .... = ... gallons

.... gallons
[3]

[Total 5 marks]

2   Temperature can be measured in °C and °F.

The table below shows three temperatures in both
degrees Celsius (°C) and degrees Fahrenheit (°F).

Celsius (°C)	10	20	30
Fahrenheit (°F)	50	68	86

a) Plot the points and join them with a straight line to draw
a conversion graph to change between °C and °F.
[2]

b) Use your graph to find 26 °C in °F.

.... °F
[1]

c) Use your graph to find 96 °F in °C.

.... °C
[1]

[Total 4 marks]

Score:

9

Section Three — Graphs

Real-Life Graphs

1 A laundry service charges a flat fee of £5, plus £1 per item washed.

a) Complete the table below.

Number of items	0	5	10	20
Cost (£)	5			25

[2]

b) Use the information in the table above to draw a graph. *[2]*

c) Use your graph to work out how many items of clothing could be washed for £30.

....

[1]

[Total 5 marks]

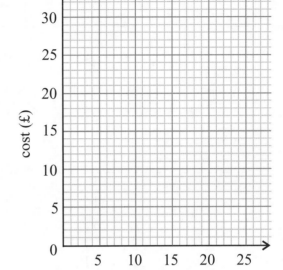

2 An electricity company offers its customers two different price plans.

Plan A:
Monthly rate of , plus 10p for each unit used.

Plan B:
No monthly rate, just pay for each unit used.

Some of the information is missing.

a) Use the graph to find:
  (i) The monthly rate for Plan **A**.

£ ....

[1]

  (ii) The cost per unit for Plan **B**.

.... p

[2]

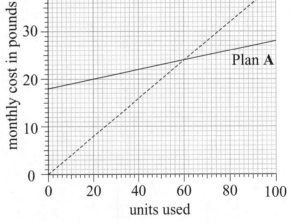

*b) Mr Barker uses about 85 units of electricity each month.
Which price plan would you advise him to choose? Explain your answer.

....

....

[2]

[Total 5 marks]

Score:

10

Quadratic Graphs

1 A table of values for $y = x^2 - 5$ is shown below.

x	-3	-2	-1	0	1	2
y	4	-1	-4	-5	-4	-1

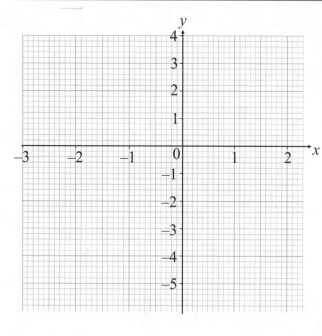

a) Draw the graph of $y = x^2 - 5$ on the grid.

[2]

b) Use your graph to estimate the negative solution to the equation $x^2 - 5 = 0$. Give your answer to 1 decimal place.

$x = $ ....

[1]

[Total 3 marks]

Don't use a ruler to join up the dots in curved graphs.

2 This question is about the equation $y = x(x + 2)$.

a) Complete the table of values on the right for the equation $y = x(x + 2)$.

x	-4	-3	-2	-1	0	1	2
y	8		0		0	3	8

[1]

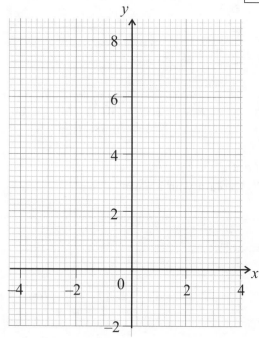

b) On the grid, draw the graph of $y = x(x + 2)$ from $x = -4$ to $x = 2$.

[2]

c) The area of a rectangular paddling pool is 6 m². Given that it is 2 metres longer than it is wide, estimate the width of the paddling pool.

.... m

[2]

[Total 5 marks]

Score:

8

Section Three — Graphs

Symmetry

1   Below are some incomplete patterns.

a) Shade in four more squares in the grid below so that line AB is a line of symmetry.

[1]

b) Shade in six more squares so that the grid below has exactly two lines of symmetry.

[1]

[Total 2 marks]

2   Below is a pattern made by shading part of a square grid.

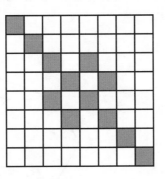

a) Draw all the lines of symmetry for the pattern.

[2]

b) What is the order of rotational symmetry of the pattern?

....

[1]

[Total 3 marks]

3 Each shape below is made with five small squares.

A   B   C   D   E

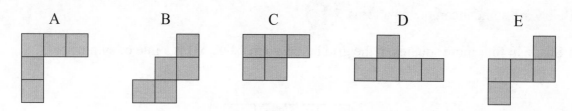

a) Two of the shapes have one line of symmetry.
   Write down the letters of these shapes.

.... and ....

[2]

b) Which shape has rotational symmetry of order 2?

....

[1]

Shape D is redrawn on the right.

c) Add one more square to the diagram so that
   shape D has rotational symmetry of order **2**.

[1]

[Total 4 marks]

4 The diagram below shows a prism.

 Draw in **one** plane of symmetry for the prism on the diagram.

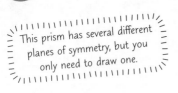
This prism has several different planes of symmetry, but you only need to draw one.

[Total 2 marks]

Score:

11

Properties of 2D Shapes

1   Below are four shapes.

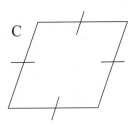

a) What is the mathematical name of shape A? ....

[1]

b) Which of these shapes is a rhombus? Write down the letter.

....

[1]

[Total 2 marks]

2   Draw a quadrilateral that has 2 pairs of equal sides and 2 pairs of equal angles.

[Total 2 marks]

3   Draw a trapezium on the grid below.

[Total 1 mark]

4   Below is a parallelogram.

a) How many lines of symmetry does a parallelogram have?

....

[1]

b) What order of rotational symmetry does a parallelogram have?

....

[1]

[Total 2 marks]

Score: ☐

7

Congruence and Similarity

1 Look at the shapes below.

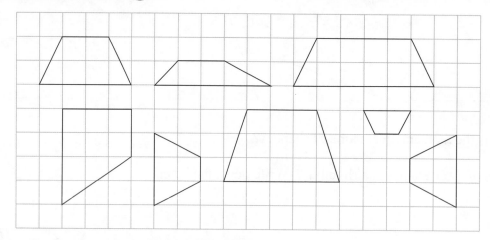

a) Write C in the two shapes that are **congruent**.

[1]

b) Write S in the two shapes that are **similar**.

[1]

[Total 2 marks]

2 The shape below has been divided into triangles.

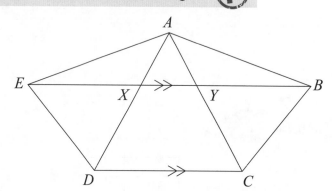

a) Which triangle in this diagram is congruent to triangle *ABY*?

....

[1]

b) Which triangle is similar to triangle *ACD*?

....

[1]

[Total 2 marks]

3 Write down the letters of 2 different pairs of congruent shapes.

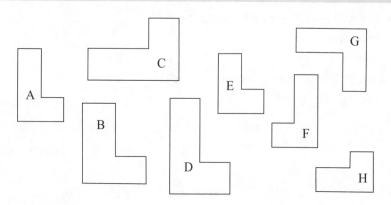

.... and ....

.... and ....

[Total 2 marks]

Score:

6

3D Shapes

1   Write down the mathematical names of the 3D shapes below.

    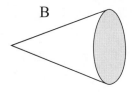

A ....

[1]

B ....

[1]

[Total 2 marks]

2   Thomas is making toffee for Christmas presents.

He wants to make boxes to put his toffee in.
He works out that he needs a cuboid as
shown on the right.

How many of the following does the cuboid have?

a) Faces

....

[1]

b) Edges

....

[1]

c) Vertices

....

[1]

[Total 3 marks]

3   Below are four 3D shapes.

           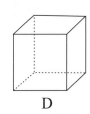

A   B   C   D

a) What is the name of shape A?   ....

[1]

b) How many faces does shape D have?

....

[1]

c) Which shape has 9 edges?

....

[1]

d) Which shape has the most vertices?

....

[1]

[Total 4 marks]

Score:

9

Projections

1 The diagram below shows the front elevation and plan view of a house.

Draw the side elevation of the house.

Front elevation   Plan view

Side elevation

[Total 3 marks]

2 The diagram below shows a solid made from identical cubes.
The side elevation of the solid is drawn on the adjacent grid.

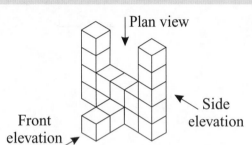

Plan view

Side elevation

Front elevation

Side elevation

On the grids below, draw the front elevation and plan view of the solid.

Front elevation   Plan view   *[Total 4 marks]*

3 Shapes X and Y are made from solid cubes.

Match each view below to an arrow.
Write the correct letter underneath each view.

←B

A   Shape **X**

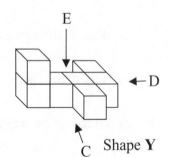

E

←D

C   Shape **Y**

....

Score:

11

[Total 4 marks]

Section Four — Shapes and Area

Perimeters and Areas

1   The shape below is drawn on a grid of centimetre squares.

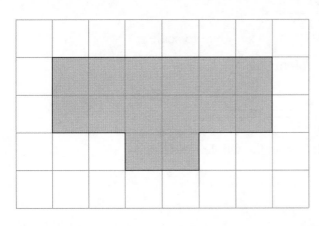

a) What is the perimeter of the shape?

.... cm
[1]

b) What is the area of the shape?

.... cm²
[1]

[Total 2 marks]

2   The diagram below shows a rectangle and a square.

Not to scale

a) Calculate the area of the rectangle.

.... cm²
[2]

b) The rectangle and the square have the same area.
What is the length of each side of the square?

.... cm
[2]

[Total 4 marks]

3   The diagram below shows a rectangle with a right-angled triangle inside.

Calculate the area of the shaded part.

.... cm²
[Total 5 marks]

Section Four — Shapes and Area

56

4 The diagram shows a field. A farmer wants to spray weedkiller on the field. Weedkiller costs £0.27 per 10 m².

How much will it cost the farmer to spray weedkiller on the whole field?

£ ....
[Total 4 marks]

FUNCTIONAL

5 Lynn is designing a garden. The diagram shows her design.

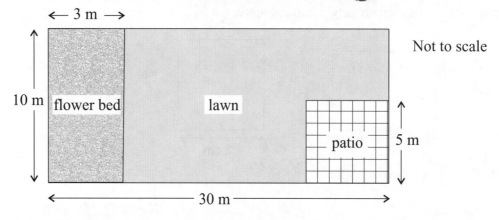

Lynn's garden will be rectangular, with a rectangular flower bed at one end, and a square patio at the other end. The rest of the space is taken up by a lawn.

a) The grass seed that Lynn is planning to use comes in boxes that cost £7 each. Each box will cover 10 m². How much will it cost Lynn to plant the lawn?

£ ....
[6]

b) Lynn wants to put a decorative border all around the edges of the lawn. Lawn edging is sold in 2 metre strips. How many strips should Lynn buy?

....
[3]

[Total 9 marks]

Score:

24

Section Four — Shapes and Area

Circles

1   The diagram shows a circle with centre O.
     A, B and C are points on the circle.

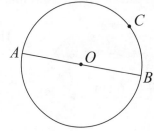

   a) What is the term given to the line AB?

     ....
                                                [1]

   b) Draw a straight line from the centre, O, to the edge of the circle.
      What is the term given to this line?

                                  ....
                                                [1]

   c) Draw a straight line connecting points B and C.
      What is the term given to this line?

                                  ....
                                                [1]

   d) At point A, draw a tangent to the circle.

                                                [1]

                                       [Total 4 marks]

2   The radius of a circle is 0.25 m.

     Calculate the circumference of the circle.
     Use $\pi = 3.14$ in this calculation.

                                                      0.25 m
                                  Not to scale

                              .... m
                                       [Total 2 marks]

3   The diagram shows six identical chocolate biscuits on a rectangular tray.

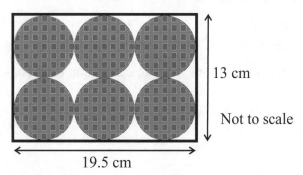

13 cm

Not to scale

19.5 cm

   a) Calculate the area of the tray.   .... cm²
                                                                        [2]

   b) Calculate the area of one chocolate biscuit.
      Give your answer in cm² to 1 decimal place.   .... cm²
                                                                        [3]

                                       [Total 5 marks]

Section Four — Shapes and Area

4 A letter "O" is formed by cutting a circular section from the centre of a circular piece of card.

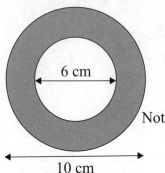

The diameter of the inside circle is 6 cm.
The diameter of the outside circle is 10 cm.

Calculate the area of the shaded region of the letter "O".
Give your answer to 3 significant figures.

Not to scale

.... cm²

[Total 4 marks]

FUNCTIONAL

5 Lucas has a square garden with sides of length 8 metres.
The garden contains a circular paved area.

Lucas wants to sow grass seed on the unpaved parts (shaded below).

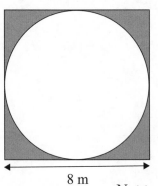

A packet of grass seeds will sow 0.5 m² of grass.
Calculate the number of packets that Lucas needs to buy.

Area of square = ... × .... = ... m²

Area of circle = π × .... = ... m²

Area of grass = ... − .... = ... m²

Number of packets of grass seed = ... ÷ 0.5 = ...

8 m

Not to scale

....

[Total 6 marks]

FUNCTIONAL

6 Zara is making cookies for a baking competition.
She makes them exactly 10 cm in diameter.

Zara wants to decorate the cookies with chocolate buttons.
She works out that there needs to be at least 3 cm² for each button.

What is the maximum number of buttons that she can put on each cookie?

Not to scale

....

[Total 5 marks]

Volume

1 The diagram below shows a prism made from centimetre cubes.

Calculate the volume of the prism.

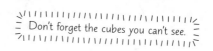
Don't forget the cubes you can't see.

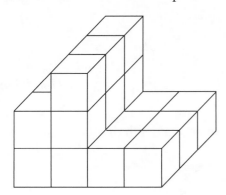

.... cm³

[Total 2 marks]

2 The diagram shows an open-topped cardboard box in the shape of a cuboid.

Calculate the volume of the box.

14 cm

6 cm

10 cm

Not to scale

.... cm³

[Total 2 marks]

FUNCTIONAL

3 The diagram below shows Amy's new paddling pool.
It has a diameter of 2 metres, and is 40 cm high.

Not to scale

40 cm

2 m

Calculate the volume of water if the paddling pool is completely full.
Give your answer in m³ to 2 decimal places.

Area of cross-section = π × .... = ...

Volume of paddling pool = ... × area of cross-section

= .... × ....

= ....

.... m³

[Total 3 marks]

4 Find the volume of the triangular prism shown below.

5 cm

4 cm

4 cm   6 cm

Not to scale

.... cm³

[Total 3 marks]

5 A fish tank of length 90 cm and width 30 cm is filled with water to a depth of 40 cm.

Not to scale

40 cm

30 cm

90 cm

a) Calculate the volume of water in the tank.

.... cm³

[2]

b) To avoid overcrowding in the tank, each fish needs 6000 cm³ of water.
Work out the greatest number of fish the tank will hold.

....

[2]

[Total 4 marks]

FUNCTIONAL

*6 A company makes boxes of fudge. Each box is a cube with a side length of 8 cm.

The fudge is packed and sent in packing cases that have length 50 cm,
width 40 cm and height 16 cm. What is the maximum number of fudge
boxes that can be packed into each case?

Not to scale

16 cm

50 cm

40 cm

....

[Total 3 marks]

Score:

17

Section Four — Shapes and Area

Nets and Surface Area

1 Complete the net of the cuboid below.

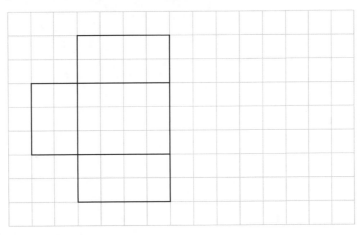

[Total 2 marks]

2 Look at the diagrams below.

   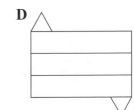

Which diagram shows the net for a triangular prism?

....

[Total 1 mark]

3 Sarah is making a box in the shape of a cuboid that is 1 cm high, 4 cm wide and 5 cm long.

a) Draw an accurate net of the box.

[3]

b) Calculate the total area of card needed to make the box.
   Assume that no overlap is needed.

.... cm²

[3]

[Total 6 marks]

Section Four — Shapes and Area

4 Here is a square-based pyramid.

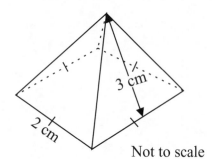

Not to scale

Draw an accurate net of the pyramid on the centimetre grid on the right.

[Total 3 marks]

FUNCTIONAL

5 Dan has bought a new door for his garden shed. He needs to varnish the door all over to make sure that it is weatherproof. The door is 2 m high, 1 m wide, and 3 cm thick.

One tin of varnish will cover 2.45 m² of wood, and Dan will need to give the door two coats of varnish. How many tins should he buy?

Make sure you convert all the measurements into the same units.

....

[Total 4 marks]

6 The diagram shows a regular octahedron and one of its faces. Each of the faces is an equilateral triangle.

Calculate the surface area of the octahedron.

Area of triangle = $\frac{1}{2}$ × .... × ....

= .... cm²

Surface area of octahedron = ... × ....

= .... cm²

Not to scale

5.2 cm

6.0 cm

.... cm²

[Total 3 marks]

Score:

19

Section Four — Shapes and Area

Measuring and Drawing Lines and Angles

1   *AB* is a straight line. **G**

A ————————————————————————————— B

a) Measure the length of *AB*.

.... cm

[1]

b) Mark the midpoint of the line *AB* with a cross.

[1]

[Total 2 marks]

2   Triangle *ABC* is shown below.

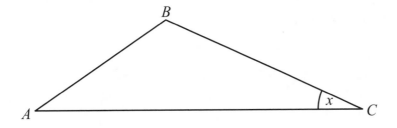

a) Mark with a cross the point on the line AB that is 2.5 cm from A. **G**

[1]

b) Measure the length of the line *AC*. Give your answer in centimetres. **G**

.... cm

[1]

c) Measure the angle *BAC*. **F**

.... °

[1]

d) Write down the special name for the type of angle marked *x*. **F**

....

[1]

[Total 4 marks]

3   The diagram shows an angle. **F**

What is the special name for this type of angle?

....

[Total 1 mark]

64

4 The diagram below shows a quadrilateral.

a) Mark a right angle with the letter R. (G)

[1]

b) Measure the length in centimetres of the line *AD*. (G)

.... cm

[1]

c) Write down the special name for the type of angle marked *x*. (F)

....

[1]

d) Measure the size of the angle *x*. (F)

..............................°

[1]

[Total 4 marks]

5 Here is a sketch of triangle *XYZ*. (F)

Draw an accurate diagram of triangle *XYZ* in the space below.

[Total 3 marks]

Five Angle Rules

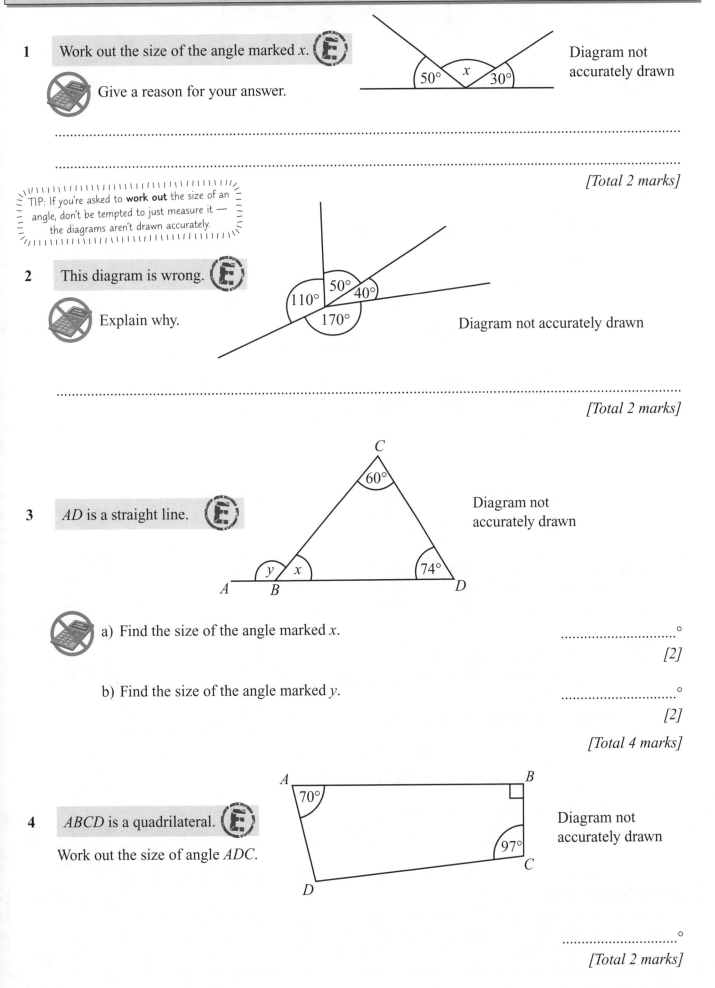

1 Work out the size of the angle marked *x*. **E**

Give a reason for your answer.

50° *x* 30°

Diagram not accurately drawn

....

....

[Total 2 marks]

TIP: If you're asked to **work out** the size of an angle, don't be tempted to just measure it — the diagrams aren't drawn accurately.

2 This diagram is wrong. **E**

Explain why.

110° 50° 40° 170°

Diagram not accurately drawn

....

[Total 2 marks]

3 *AD* is a straight line. **E**

C 60° 74° *y* *x* *A* *B* *D*

Diagram not accurately drawn

a) Find the size of the angle marked *x*.

.............................°

[2]

b) Find the size of the angle marked *y*.

.............................°

[2]

[Total 4 marks]

4 *ABCD* is a quadrilateral. **E**

Work out the size of angle *ADC*.

A 70° *B* 97° *C* *D*

Diagram not accurately drawn

.............................°

[Total 2 marks]

Section Five — Angles and Geometry

5 ABC is an isosceles triangle.
AB = BC.
AD is a straight line.

Diagram not accurately drawn

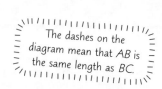
The dashes on the diagram mean that AB is the same length as BC.

Work out the size of angle BCD.

.............................°

[Total 3 marks]

---

*6 BCDE is a quadrilateral. Angle CDE is a right angle. AF is a straight line.

Diagram not accurately drawn

Work out the size of the angle marked x.
Give reasons for each stage of your working.

.............................°

[Total 5 marks]

---

*7 VXY is an isosceles triangle. VX = XY.
UVY is a right-angled triangle.
XZ is a straight line.

Diagram not accurately drawn

Work out the size of angle UYZ.
Give reasons for each stage of your working.

Angles in a triangle add up to ....

.... − 96° = ..., so angle VYX = ... ÷ 2 = ...,

because isosceles triangles have ....

Angles on a straight line add up to ....,

so angle UYZ = 180° − 90° − .... = ...

.............................°

[Total 4 marks]

Exam Practice Tip

If you can't see how to find the angle you've been asked for, try finding other angles in the diagram first — chances are you'll be able to use them to find the one you need. You'll probably have to use a few of the angle rules to get to the answer — if you get stuck just try each rule until you get to one that you can use.

Score

22

Section Five — Angles and Geometry

Parallel Lines

1 This is an accurately drawn quadrilateral.

a) Mark with arrows a pair of parallel lines.

[1]

b) Which line is perpendicular to line QR?

....

[1]

[Total 2 marks]

2 Find the size of the angle marked a.
Give a reason for your answer.

....

[Total 2 marks]

3 AD and EG are parallel.
HG and FK are straight lines.

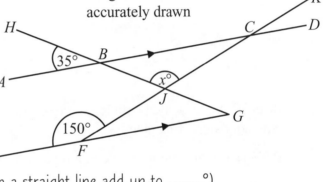

Work out the value of x.

Angle JBC = ...° (vertically opposite angles)

Angle BCK = ...° (corresponding angles)

Angle $BCJ = 180° -$ ....° = ...° (angles on a straight line add up to ....°)

$x° =$ ....° $- ($..............° $+$ ....°$) =$ ....° (angles in a triangle add up to ....°)

....

[Total 3 marks]

4 AC and DF are parallel.
GD is a straight line.
CDE is an isosceles triangle.

Find the size of the angle marked x.

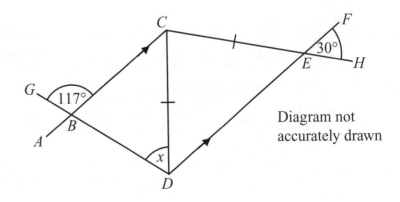

.................................°

[Total 3 marks]

Score:

10

Section Five — Angles and Geometry

Polygons and Angles

1 What is the name of the shape below?

....

[Total 1 mark]

2 The diagram shows a pentagon.

 Work out the size of the angle *p*.

Not to scale

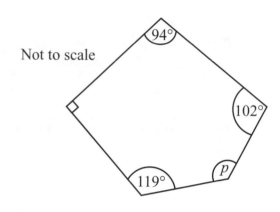

..........................°

[Total 4 marks]

3 Kate's kitchen is tiled with regular hexagons and equilateral triangles.

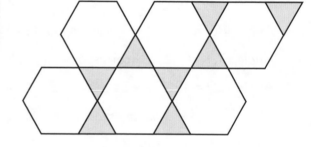

a) Work out the interior angle of a regular hexagon.

Exterior angle = 360° ÷ ....

= ....

Interior angle = 180° — .... = ...°

[2]

*b) Explain why regular hexagons and equilateral triangles can fit together with no gaps.

Each angle in an equilateral triangle is 60°. The interior angle of a regular hexagon is   °.

Angles round a point add up to   °.

60° +   ° +   ° +   ° =   °, so 2 regular hexagons and 2 equilateral triangles

can meet at a point.

[3]

[Total 5 marks]

Exam Practice Tip

Don't panic if you get an 'Explain why...' question on polygons — all you're being asked to do is use the rules you know about angles. If you just remember that the exterior angles of a polygon add up to 360°, angles on a line add up to 180° and angles round a point add up to 360°, you should be fine.

Score

10

Transformations

1 Reflect the shaded shape in the mirror line.

TIP: Take each corner one by one, reflect it, and then join them all up.

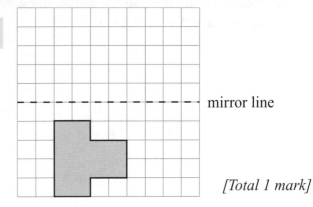

mirror line

[Total 1 mark]

2 Triangle **A** has been drawn on the grid below.

Reflect triangle **A** in the line $x = -1$. Label your image **B**.

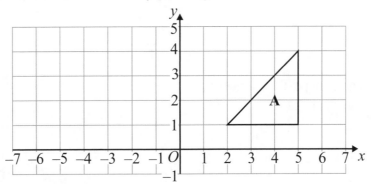

[Total 2 marks]

3 The grid shows triangle **P** and triangle **Q**.

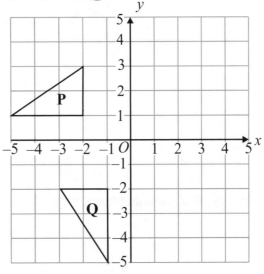

a) Rotate triangle **P** 90° clockwise about the point $(-1, -1)$. *[3]*

b) Describe fully the single transformation that maps triangle **P** onto triangle **Q**.

....

[3]

[Total 6 marks]

Section Five — Angles and Geometry

4 The grid to the right shows shape **A** and shape **B**. (D)

a) Describe fully the single transformation that maps shape **A** onto shape **B**.

....

....

[2]

b) Reflect shape **A** in the line $y = x$. Label the image **C**.

[2]

c) Describe fully the single transformation that maps shape **C** onto shape **B**.

....

[3]

[Total 7 marks]

5 Shape **R**, shape **S** and shape **T** have been drawn on the grid to the right.

a) Translate shape **T** by the vector $\begin{pmatrix} -1 \\ 3 \end{pmatrix}$. (D) *[1]*

b) Describe fully the single transformation that maps shape **T** onto shape **R**. (D)

....

[2]

c) Describe fully the single transformation that maps shape **R** onto shape **S**. (C)

....

....

[3]

[Total 6 marks]

6 On the grid enlarge the triangle by a scale factor of 3, centre (−4, 0).

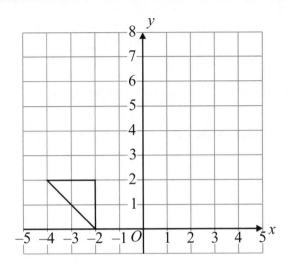

[Total 3 marks]

7 Shape **A** has been drawn on the grid.

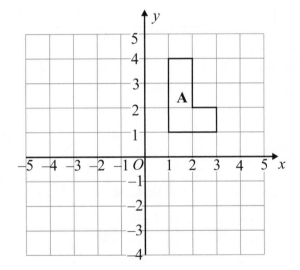

Shape **A** is reflected in the *x*-axis to give shape **B**.
Shape **B** is rotated 180° about the origin to give shape **C**.

Describe fully the single transformation which maps shape **A** onto shape **C**.

....

[Total 4 marks]

Score

29

Similar Shape Problems

1   Triangle **A** is enlarged by a scale factor of 3 to give triangle **B**.

Write down whether each statement below is true or false.

a) The angles of triangle **B** are the same size as the angles of triangle **A**.

....

[1]

b) The sides of triangle **B** are 3 times as long as the sides of triangle **A**.

....

[1]

c) The area of triangle **B** is 3 times as big as the area of triangle **A**.

....

[1]

[Total 3 marks]

2   Diagrams of two flags are shown below.

Flag **Q** is an enlargement of flag **P** by a scale factor of 2.5.

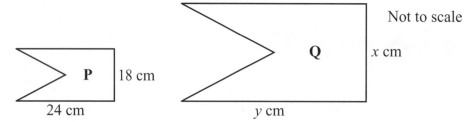

Not to scale

Find the value of x and the value of y.

$x =$ .... and $y =$ ....

[Total 2 marks]

3   Draw an enlargement of the shaded shape, scale factor 2, on the grid.

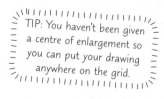
TIP: You haven't been given a centre of enlargement so you can put your drawing anywhere on the grid.

[Total 2 marks]

Score:

7

Triangle Construction

1 Side *BC* of the equilateral triangle *ABC* has been accurately drawn below.

B ———————————————————— C

a) Use a ruler and compasses to complete the accurate drawing of triangle *ABC*.   *[1]*

b) Construct the bisector of angle *ACB* of the triangle.   *[2]*
   You must show all your construction lines.

[Total 3 marks]

2 The diagram below is a sketch of triangle *ABC*.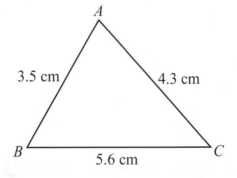

Not to scale

Use a ruler and compasses to make an accurate drawing of triangle *ABC* in the space below.
You must show all your construction lines.

[Total 3 marks]

Score: ☐

6

 ☐   ☐   ☐

Loci and Constructions

1 Construct a regular hexagon so that each vertex lies on the circle below.

You must show all your construction lines.

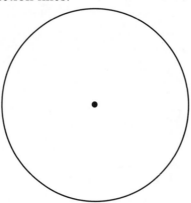

[Total 3 marks]

2 Two sides of quadrilateral *PQRS* have been accurately drawn below.
The other two sides are side *PS* and side *RS*. Side *PS* is 4.2 cm and side *RS* is 6.7 cm.

You must show all your construction lines.

a) Use a ruler and compasses to accurately complete the quadrilateral.   *[2]*

b) Construct the perpendicular to the line segment *PQ* that passes through point *R*. ⓒ   *[2]*

[Total 4 marks]

3 Salman has a robot which can walk a maximum of 10 m from the beam *AB*. ⓒ

Shade the region on the diagram where Salman's robot can walk, using the scale shown.

Scale: 1 cm represents 5 m

[Total 2 marks]

4 A town council wants to put up a new visitor information board. They think that it should be placed closer to the park than to the library, but also closer to the station than to the park.

The diagram below shows a scale map of the town centre.
Shade in the region of the town where the board could be placed.

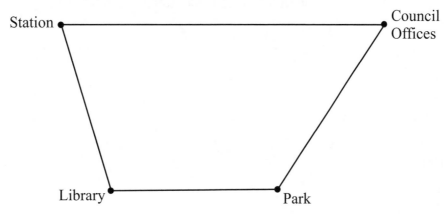

[Total 5 marks]

5 Hilary and Tony are deciding where they would like to put a pond in their garden. Hilary wants the centre of the pond to be 1 m from the garden wall *BC*. Tony wants the centre of the pond to be 2 m from the tree *F*.

Accurately complete the plan of the garden below by using a cross (✕) to mark any points where Hilary and Tony would both be happy for the centre of the pond to be.

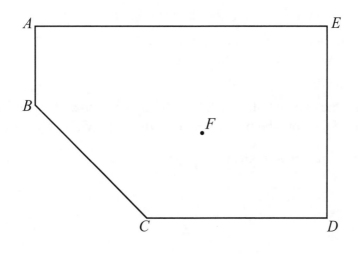

Scale: 1 cm represents 1 m

[Total 4 marks]

Exam Practice Tip

You won't always be told that you need to use a ruler and compasses, but if you're asked to <u>construct</u> something then you'll be expected to use them. Make sure you don't rub out your construction lines — even if it doesn't ask for them in the question you won't get all the marks unless you show how you did your construction.

Score

18

Pythagoras' Theorem

1 A 3.5 m long ladder is resting against a vertical wall and on the horizontal ground. For safety the bottom of the ladder must be at least 2.1 m away from the wall.

How far up the wall can the ladder safely reach?

3.5 m

2.1 m

.... m

[Total 3 marks]

FUNCTIONAL

*2 Alison and Rob want to put a water pipe across their rectangular field. The diagram below shows their field.

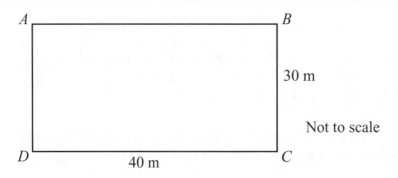

30 m

Not to scale

40 m

TIP: Draw a quick sketch using the information that you're given in the question — then you can easily see where to put the numbers in the Pythagoras formula.

The pipe must run from a tap at point at *A* to the shed at point *C*.

Alison wants to put the pipe across the diagonal of the field.
Rob wants to put the pipe round the edge of the field.

The pipe costs £8.35 per metre.

If they put the pipe across the diagonal they will have to dig a trench and replace the grass, which will cost £202.50. If they put the pipe round the edge they will not have to dig a trench.

Which option is cheaper? Explain your answer.

....

....

[Total 6 marks]

Exam Practice Tip

You probably won't be <u>told</u> to use Pythagoras' theorem in the question — you'll have to remember it's something you can use if you've got two sides of a right-angled triangle and you're looking for the third side.
If you get a wordy question it's a good idea to sketch a diagram to make sure your sides are in the right place.

Score

9

Units and Conversions

1 The table below shows different units of measurements.

a) Complete the table using the most appropriate unit of measurement.

	Imperial	Metric
Length of a car	feet	....
Weight of a rabbit	....	kilograms
Volume of a milk jug	pints	....

[3]

b) The length of a classroom is 887 cm. How long is that in metres?

.... m

[1]

c) A bunch of bananas weighs 1.3 kg. How much is this in grams?

.... g

[1]

[Total 5 marks]

FUNCTIONAL

2 Emma is having a party with some friends.

  She has 2.5 litres of orange juice.
How many 250 ml cups can be filled from it?

.... cups

[Total 3 marks]

FUNCTIONAL

3 Nicole wants to post some books to a friend in another country.
Each book weighs 1.5 lb and each package can hold a maximum weight of 2500 g.

How many books can she send in one package?

Hint — 1 kg ≈ 2.2 lb

....

[Total 4 marks]

4 The formula to convert kilometres (k) to miles (m) is $m = \dfrac{5k}{8}$.

a) How many miles is 40 km? **(E)**

.... miles

[2]

b) A giraffe can run at 60 km/h.
Show that a giraffe could be outrun by a camel running at 40 mph. **(D)**

....

....

[2]

[Total 4 marks]

FUNCTIONAL

5 1 litre = $1\frac{3}{4}$ pints. **(D)**

You could start by converting 14 pints into litres.

Margaret needs 14 pints of water to fill up her fish tank.
She uses three different sized containers to fill up the tank.
One container holds 520 ml, one holds 540 ml and the other holds 720 ml.

To fill up the tank, Margaret uses the 720 ml container three times,
the 520 ml container five times and then the 540 ml container to finish filling it up.

How many times must she fill up the 540 ml container to finish filling the fish tank?

....

[Total 5 marks]

6 The playing surface of a snooker table has an area of 39 200 cm². **(D)**

Convert the area of the snooker table into m².

.... m²

[Total 2 marks]

Exam Practice Tip

Make sure you learn the rough conversions between metric units (kg, km, cm and litres) and imperial units (pounds, miles, feet, gallons and pints). I know it's dull just memorising numbers, but you might not be given them in the exam. You also need to know metric-to-metric conversions, but thankfully those are MUCH easier.

Score

23

Section Six — Measures

Reading Scales

1   Give the readings from each of the scales below.

a)

.... °C
[1]

b)

c)

.... mph
[1]

.... oz
[1]

[Total 3 marks]

2   Francis has a bottle of ink, as shown below.

a) How much ink does he have left in the bottle?

.... ml
[1]

b) Francis uses 15 ml of the ink.
   How much does he now have left?

.... ml
[2]

[Total 3 marks]

3   Alex is competing in a javelin competition.

a) Her best throw of the day is shown below. How far did she throw?

.... m
[1]

b) Martin threw the javelin 42.4 m. Mark his throw on the tape measure above.

[1]

[Total 2 marks]

Score:

8

Rounding and Estimating Measurements

1 The man in this picture is of average height.

Use this information to estimate the height of the penguin.

.... cm

[Total 3 marks]

2 Mandy uses a thermometer to measure the temperature outside.

a) The thermometer on the left shows the temperature first thing in the morning.
Write down the temperature. **F**

.... °C
[1]

b) By the afternoon the temperature is 1.2 °C.
Mark the temperature on the thermometer to the right.
[1]

c) The next morning, Mandy records the temperature as 3 °C to the nearest degree.
What is the minimum temperature her thermometer could show in order for her to record this temperature?

.... °C
[1]

[Total 3 marks]

3 Joseph is weighing himself. His scales give his weight to the nearest kilogram. **C**

According to his scales, Joseph is 57 kg.
What are the minimum and maximum weights that he could be?

Minimum weight: .... kg

Maximum weight: .... kg

[Total 2 marks]

Score:

8

Reading Timetables

1   Amir flies from London to Kuala Lumpur, setting off in the morning. **(F)**

a) The clock shows the time when the flight leaves.
What time is shown on the clock?

....
[1]

b) The time in Kuala Lumpur is 8 hours ahead of the time in London.
What time is it in Kuala Lumpur when it is 10:30 am in London.?

....
[1]

[Total 2 marks]

2   Deirdre is planning a train journey. **(F)**

a) It will take 25 minutes to get to the station and she wants to be there at 11 15.
What is the latest time she should leave home?

....
[2]

b) The train leaves at 11 35 and arrives at 13 22.
How long is the journey? Give your answer in minutes.

.... minutes
[2]

[Total 4 marks]

3   Part of the bus timetable from Coventry to Rugby is shown below.

Coventry	14 45	16 15	17 45
Bubbenhall	–	16 40	18 10
Stretton	15 14	16 54	18 24
Birdingbury	–	17 04	–
Rugby	15 35	17 30	18 40

The dashes on the timetable mean the bus doesn't stop.

a) What time does the 16 15 bus from Coventry leave Birdingbury? **(F)**

....
[1]

b) Lisa arrives at Birdingbury bus stop at 16 58. **(F)**
How long will she have to wait for the bus to Rugby?

.... minutes
[1]

The 16 15 bus from Coventry continues to Lutterworth after Rugby. It arrives in Lutterworth at 18 15.

c) Anne lives in Bubbenhall. If she catches this bus from her home, **(E)**
how long will it take her to get to Lutterworth?

.... h .... mins
[2]

[Total 4 marks]

Score: ☐
10

Compass Directions and Bearings

1 The plan of an adventure park is shown below. The square each ride is located in can be given by a letter and a number, for example Water Splash is in B3.

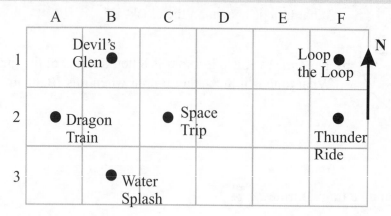

a) Which square is Thunder Ride in?

....

[1]

b) Which ride is North East of Dragon Train?

....

[1]

c) Which ride is due East of Space Trip?

....

[1]

d) If you stand at Space Trip and look towards Water Splash, which direction are you looking in?

....

[1]

[Total 4 marks]

2 The diagram shows the positions of two points on a map.

X is the top of a mountain. *Y* is the location of a group of hikers.

a) A hiker is injured, and the rescue team need to know the location of the hikers. Measure and write down the bearing of *Y* from *X*.

.............................°

[1]

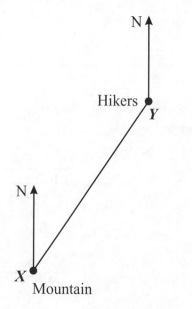

b) There is another group of hikers at a bearing of 100° from *Y*.
Draw a line on the diagram to show the direction of the second group.

[1]

[Total 2 marks]

Score: ☐

6

Section Six — Measures

 ☐   ☐   ☐

Maps and Scale Drawings

1 Douglas drew a scale drawing of his dining room.

a) His dining table is 2 m long.
   What is the scale of this drawing?

   1 cm to .... m
   [1]

b) Work out the real distance from
   the dining table to the shelves.

   .... m
   [1]

c) What is the real area of the dining room?

   .... m²
   [3]

   [Total 5 marks]

2 This map is drawn to a scale of 1 : 200 000.

River
Arkben

Clandon

Benton

Arkburgh

Scale 1 : 200 000

a) Work out the actual distance, in km, between Arkburgh and Benton.

   .... km
   [1]

b) Madeline cycles 7 km to school. How far would this be on the map?

   .... cm
   [1]

   [Total 2 marks]

Score: ⬜

7

 ⬜   ⬜   ⬜

Speed and Density

1   John and Alan hired a van. Their receipt gave them information about how much time they spent travelling in the van, and how fast they went.

> Travelling time: 1 hour 15 minutes
> Average Speed: 56 km/h

Calculate the distance that John and Alan travelled in the van.

.... km

[Total 2 marks]

*2   Beatrix is on a cycling holiday in Cumbria.
The table below shows the distances between each of the places she visits.

Keswick		
26 miles	Windermere	
33 miles	5 miles	Hawkshead

On Friday it took her 45 minutes to cycle from Hawkshead to Windermere.

On Saturday, she then cycled from Windermere, arriving in Keswick $3\frac{1}{4}$ hours later.

On Sunday, she cycled back from Keswick to Hawkshead in 3 hours 45 minutes.

On which day did Beatrix ride her bike at the fastest average speed?

....

[Total 4 marks]

3   The mass of a metal statue is 360 kg.
The density of the metal alloy from which it is made is 1800 kg/m³.

Calculate the volume of the statue.

.... m³

[Total 2 marks]

Score:

8

Collecting Data

1 Faye wants to find out how often teenagers buy chocolate bars.

She writes the following question to ask in a survey.

> How many chocolate bars have you bought?
>
> 1 – 2   2 – 3   3 – 4
>
> ☐   ☐   ☐

Write two things that are wrong with the question above.

1. ....

2. ....

[Total 2 marks]

2 Mike wants to find out how often people in his year group go to watch football matches.

He includes the question below in a survey.

> How often do you go to watch football matches?
>
> Sometimes   A lot
>
> ☐   ☐

a) Give **one** thing that is wrong with this question.

....

....

[1]

Mike decides to ask the boys in his football team to do his survey.

b) Give one reason why this sample may not give him reliable information.

....

....

[1]

[Total 2 marks]

Exam Practice Tip

In the exam, you might be asked to say why a particular survey question isn't very good. Always look at two things — the way it's worded and whether the response boxes are suitable. You might also get asked why a particular sample isn't good. Bias is often the problem here — think about whether the sample is representative.

Score

☐

4

 ☐   ☐   ☐

Mean, Median, Mode and Range

1 One evening Preya makes 10 phone calls. When the bill comes it shows how long each call was, in minutes. The call lengths are listed below. **(F)**

   10   12   25   3   37   13   12   18   41   33

   a) Work out the median length of Preya's calls.

   .... minutes
   [2]

   b) Calculate the mean phone call length.
      Give your answer to the nearest minute.

   .... minutes
   [2]

   c) What is the range?

   .... minutes
   [2]

   [Total 6 marks]

2 Company A employs 5 people.
   Their annual salaries are listed below.

   £18 000   £38 500   £18 000   £25 200   £18 000

   a) Write down the mode. **(F)**

   £ ....
   [1]

   b) What is the median annual salary? **(F)**

   £ ....
   [1]

   Company B has a mean annual salary of £24 150.
   c) Compare the mean annual salary of Company A and Company B. **(E)**

   ....

   ....

   [3]

   [Total 5 marks]

3 Sam thinks of three different whole numbers. **(F)**

   The numbers have a range of 6 and a mean of 4.
   What are the three numbers?

   ...., ..., ...
   [Total 2 marks]

Exam Practice Tip

Remember — the mode is the most common value, the median is the middle value (when the data is written in order), the mean is the sum of all the values divided by the number of values, and the range is the highest value minus the lowest value. It's usually a good idea to write your data in ascending order before you do anything else.

Score

13

Section Seven — Statistics and Probability

Tables

1   Ryan is looking at properties in a new development.
The table below shows information on these properties.

Property name	House/apartment	No. of bedrooms	Size (square feet)	Price (£)
The Apricot	House	5	1136	319 995
The Ivy	Apartment	2	526	119 995
The Lavender	House	3	744	189 995
The Oak	House	4	892	244 995
The Willow	Apartment	3	608	144 995

a) Which property has the fewest bedrooms?

....

[1]

b) How many of these properties are **houses** that are smaller than 1000 square feet?

....

[1]

[Total 2 marks]

FUNCTIONAL

*2   Mr and Mrs White and their three children want to go on holiday next year.
They can go for a week in either June or July.
The table below shows prices in £ per adult and per child for a week.

Departure Date	Adult	Child
01 Jan — 19 Mar	140	125
20 Mar — 21 May	180	150
22 May — 30 Jun	300	290
01 July — 8 Sep	330	275
9 Sep — 26 Nov	230	160
27 Nov — 31 Dec	270	210

Compare the cost of the White family going on holiday for a week in June with the cost
of a week in July.

....

....

....

....

....

[Total 4 marks]

Score:

6

Pictograms

1 This pictogram shows the number of jars of jam sold in a campsite shop in one month. **G**

a) How many jars of strawberry jam were sold?

....
[1]

Strawberry Jam	🍓🍓🍓🍓
Blackberry Jam	🍓🍓◖
Raspberry Jam	
🍓 Represents 10 jars	

The shop sold 35 jars of raspberry jam.
b) Complete the pictogram. *[1]*

c) Which jam did they sell the least of?

....
[1]

[Total 3 marks]

2 This pictogram shows the number of eggs laid by some chickens at a farm on Monday, Tuesday and Wednesday. **G**

Monday	◯ ◯ ◯ ◔
Tuesday	◯ ◯ ◖
Wednesday	◯ ◯ ◯ ◯ ◯
Thursday	
Friday	

◯ = 8 eggs

Pay attention to the key, which shows how many things each symbol stands for.

a) How many eggs were laid on Monday?

....
[1]

b) How many more eggs were laid on Wednesday than Tuesday?

....
[1]

24 eggs were laid on Thursday.
18 eggs were laid on Friday.
c) Show this information on the pictogram. *[2]*

[Total 4 marks]

Score:
7

Bar Charts

1 The dual bar chart below shows the number of cups of tea and coffee sold in a cafe each day.

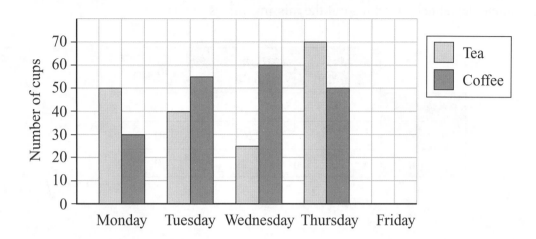

a) How many cups of tea were sold on Wednesday?

....

[1]

b) On which day did the cafe sell 15 more cups of coffee than tea?

....

[1]

On Friday, the cafe sold 45 cups of tea and 30 cups of coffee.

c) Show this information on the bar chart.

[2]

d) Over the 5 days, did the cafe sell more cups of tea or coffee?

....

[2]

[Total 6 marks]

2 This table shows some information about the favourite sports of some students.

Sport	Students
Football	14
Swimming	5
Athletics	9
Netball	1
Hockey	6

Show this information as a bar chart on the grid below.

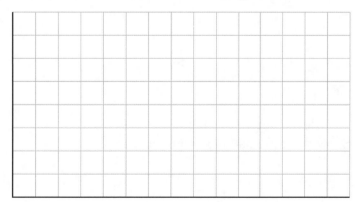

[Total 3 marks]

Score:

9

Two-Way Tables

1 200 people were asked if they were right-handed or left-handed.
The table below shows some information about the results.

  Complete the table by working out the missing values.

	Left-Handed	Right-Handed	Total
Male	9		
Female		126	140
Total	23		200

[Total 4 marks]

2 At a school sports day, the students can take part
in swimming, athletics or football.

Trey collects information on how many girls and boys took part in each sport.
a) Design a two-way table that Trey could use to display this information.

[3]

b) 32 girls took part in athletics.
   Show this information in your table above.

[1]

[Total 4 marks]

Section Seven — Statistics and Probability

Score: ____

8

Time Series

1 A newsagent records the number of ice-creams they sell each day in the summer holidays.

The results are shown in the time series graph below.

a) Use the information in the table to complete the time series graph.

Date	Number of ice-creams sold
Sun 11th Aug	24
Mon 12th Aug	23
Tue 13th Aug	34
Wed 14th Aug	35
Thu 15th Aug	35
Fri 16th Aug	36
Sat 17th Aug	36

[2]

b) Ice-cream sales increase on hot days.
On what date was it likely to be the hottest?

....

[1]

c) There were 2 days in August on which it rained.
On which dates do you think it rained?
Use the graph to explain your answer.

....

....

[2]

d) On Sunday 18th August, the weather is forecast to be
similar to the weather on Saturday 17th August.
Plot a point that could represent the number of ice-creams sold on Sunday 18th August.
Give a reason why you have chosen that point.

....

....

[2]

[Total 7 marks]

Score:

7

Section Seven — Statistics and Probability

Pie Charts

1 A survey was carried out at a leisure centre to find out which sport people prefer to do. The results are shown in the pie chart.

a) What fraction of people prefer to do fitness training?

¼

[1]

60 people said they prefer to play football.
b) How many people prefer to play badminton?

:

20

[2]

[Total 3 marks]

2 A survey was carried out in a local cinema to find out which flavour of popcorn people bought. The results are in the table below.

a) Draw a pie chart to represent the information.

Type of popcorn	Number sold
Plain	12
Salted	18
Sugared	9
Toffee	21

[3]

Another survey was carried out to find out which flavour of ice cream people bought. The results are shown in the pie chart below.

Chris compares the two pie charts and says,

"The results show that more people chose strawberry ice cream than toffee popcorn."

b) Explain whether or not Chris is right.

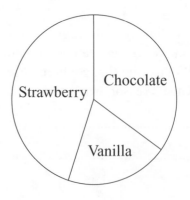

....
....
....
....

[1]

[Total 4 marks]

Score:
7

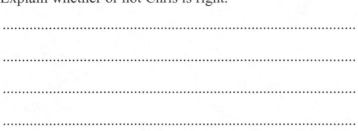

Scatter Graphs

1 In a particular class, 15 pupils study both Spanish and Italian.
Their end of year exam results are shown on the scatter graph below.

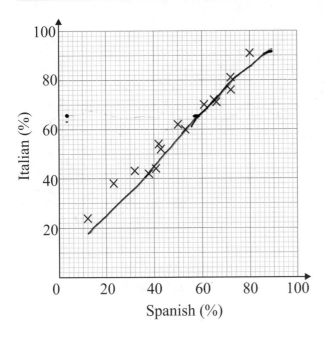

a) Give the type of correlation shown on the graph.

Positive
[1]

b) Draw a line of best fit for the data. *[1]*

c) Ahmed was absent for his Spanish exam but scored 66% on his Italian exam. Estimate the mark he might have got in Spanish.

.... %
[2]

[Total 4 marks]

2 The heights and weights of boys playing in a rugby team are shown in the scatter graph below.

Two more boys join the team. Their heights and weights are shown in the table below.

Player	Height (cm)	Weight (kg)
13	169	70
14	183	76

a) Show this information on the scatter graph.
[1]

b) The weight of one boy has not been recorded correctly. Put a ring around the cross representing this player
[1]

Another player joins the team. He is 176 cm tall.
c) Estimate how much he will weigh.

.... kg
[2]

[Total 4 marks]

Score:

8

Section Seven — Statistics and Probability

Stem and Leaf Diagrams

1 The stem and leaf diagram below shows the amount of rainfall in mm that fell on an island during a 12-day period in June.

```
0 | 8
1 | 7 9
2 | 3 6 9
3 | 0 1 4 7 8
4 | 3
```

Key
0	8 means 8 mm of rain

a) Work out the median amount of rainfall.

2̶9̶.5 .... mm
[1]

b) What is the range of rainfall?

35 .... mm
[1]

In November the median amount of rainfall was 14 mm and the range was 26 mm.

*c) Compare the amount of rainfall in November with the amount of rainfall in June.

....

....

[2]

[Total 4 marks]

2 The heights of 20 students in a class were measured to the nearest cm. The results are below.

| 165 | 163 | 159 | 148 | 162 | 167 | 155 | 158 | 173 | 169 |
| 169 | 159 | 172 | 175 | 171 | 169 | 163 | 160 | 164 | 170 |

a) Draw an ordered stem and leaf diagram to illustrate the data.

```
14 |
   |
   |
```

Key:	.... means .... cm

[3]

b) What is the modal height?

.... cm
[1]

c) How many of the students are less than 165 cm tall?

.... cm
[1]

[Total 5 marks]

Score:

9

Frequency Tables and Averages

1 Tom is having a party and wants to know whether to serve cola, orange juice, lemonade
or something else. He conducts a small survey to help him decide. He asks the question:
"Which is your favourite drink — cola, orange juice, lemonade or a different drink?"

The replies are:
Orange juice ✓ Cola ✓ Other ✓ Cola ✓ Cola ✓
Lemonade ✓ Cola Orange juice ✓ Other ✓ Orange juice
Orange juice ✓ Cola Lemonade ✓ Other ✓ Cola ✓
Other ✓ Cola ✓ Other ✓ Lemonade Orange juice ✓

Drink	Tally	Frequency
Cola	ЖИ II	7
Orange juice	ЖИ	5
Lemonade	III	3
Other	IЖ	5

a) Use the data to complete the table.

[2]

b) Which is the modal drink?

Remember — 'mode is most'.

.... Cola ....

[1]

[Total 3 marks]

2 A traffic survey at a road junction recorded the following
numbers of vehicles arriving per minute.

Vehicles per minute	0	1	2	3	4
Frequency	13	8	6	2	1

a) What is the median number of vehicles per minute?

....

[2]

b) What is the mean number of vehicles per minute?

13+8+6+2+1 = 30 / 5 = 6

6

[3]

[Total 5 marks]

Score:

8

Grouped Frequency Tables — Averages

1   As part of their coursework, the students in a Year 11 maths class recorded their arm spans. The results are shown below.

Use the mid-interval value of each arm span group to find an estimate of the mean arm span.

Arm Span, x cm	Frequency	Mid-Interval Value	Frequency × Mid-Interval Value
$120 \leq x < 130$	13	$(120 + 130) \div 2 = 125$	$13 \times 125 = \ldots$
$130 \leq x < 140$	6	$(130 + 140) \div 2 = \ldots$	$6 \times \ldots = \ldots$
$140 \leq x < 150$	4		
$150 \leq x < 160$	7		
Total			

Mean arm span = ... ÷ .... = ...

.... cm

[Total 4 marks]

2   A class of children was asked to draw a 10 cm line without a ruler, and then measure their attempt. This is a table of their results.

Length of line, x cm	Frequency
$8.5 \leq x < 9$	3
$9 \leq x < 9.5$	2
$9.5 \leq x < 10$	12
$10 \leq x < 10.5$	8
$10.5 \leq x < 11$	5

a) Which group contains the median?

....

[2]

b) What is the modal class?

....

[1]

c) Calculate an estimate of the mean length of their lines.

Hint: you should add some extra columns to the table above to help you.

.... cm

[4]

[Total 7 marks]

Score:

11

Section Seven — Statistics and Probability

Frequency Polygons

1 The grouped frequency table below shows the number of hours of homework 30 students did in one week.

Hours of Homework, x	Frequency
$0 \leq x < 2$	15
$2 \leq x < 4$	7
$4 \leq x < 6$	5
$6 \leq x < 8$	3

Draw a frequency polygon for the data using the grid on the right.

[Total 2 marks]

2 The frequency polygons below show the amount of rainfall per day in two different towns over a period of 45 days.

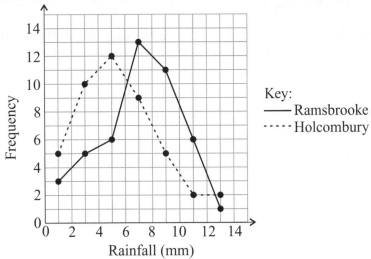

Key:
—— Ramsbrooke
----- Holcombury

a) Write down one comparison of the amount of rainfall in the two towns.

....

[1]

b) Use the frequency polygon to calculate an estimate of the mean amount of rainfall in Ramsbrooke over the 45 days.

.... mm

[3]

[Total 4 marks]

Score:

6

Section Seven — Statistics and Probability

Probability Basics

1 Eva has some picture cards.

She picks one card without looking.

Choose one of the words below to complete the sentences.

impossible   unlikely   evens   likely   certain

a) It is .... that she chooses ⬩.   *[1]*

b) It is .... that she chooses ◯.   *[1]*

c) It is .... that she chooses ⚡.   *[1]*

[Total 3 marks]

2 Ellie rolls a fair 6-sided dice. (**F**)

a) On the scale below, mark with an arrow (↑) the probability that she will roll an odd number.

0   0.5   1

[1]

b) On the scale below, mark with an arrow (↑) the probability that she will roll a 0.

0   0.5   1

[1]

c) What is the probability that Ellie rolls a number larger than 4?
Give your answer as a fraction in its simplest form.

....

[2]

[Total 4 marks]

3 Alecia has an 8-sided spinner labelled as shown on the right. (**E**)
It has an equal probability of landing on each of the 8 segments.

a) What colour segment is the spinner most likely to land on?

....

[1]

b) What is the probability of the spinner landing on a pink segment?

....

[1]

[Total 2 marks]

4 The probability that Sarah will complete a 40-mile walk is 0.13. (E)

   a) What is the probability that she will not complete the walk?
      Explain your answer.

      ....

      ....

                                                                  [2]

   b) Reisha is told that the probability of her giving birth to twins is 0.2.
      Jamie says "This means the probability of Reisha giving birth to just one baby is 0.8."
      Explain why Jamie could be wrong.

      ....

                                                                  [1]

                                                               [Total 3 marks]

5 There are 10 counters in a bag. Four of the counters are blue and the rest are red. (E)

   One counter is picked out at random.
   a) Work out the probability that the counter picked is red.
      Give your answer as a fraction in its simplest form.

                                                         ....

                                                               [2]

   b) What is the probability that the counter picked is green?

                                                          ....

                                                                [1]

                                                               [Total 3 marks]

6 Steven asks all the members of his football team whether their
   favourite position is in attack, midfield, defence or goal. (E)
   The table below shows his results.

Position	Frequency
Attack	6
Midfield	9
Defence	4
Goal	1

A member of the team is chosen at random.

What is the probability that this person's favourite position is in midfield?

                                                          ....

                                                        [Total 2 marks]

Score:

17

More Probability

1 Katie decides to attend two new after-school activities. She can do one on Monday and one on Thursday. Below are lists of the activities she could do on these days.

Monday
Hockey
Orchestra
Drama

Thursday
Netball
Choir
Orienteering

List all the possible combinations of two clubs Katie could try in one week.

[Total 2 marks]

2 Alvar has a fair 6-sided dice and a set of five cards numbered 2, 4, 6, 8 and 10. He rolls the dice and chooses a card at random. Alvar adds the number on the dice to the number on the card to calculate his total score.

a) Complete the table below to show all of the possible scores.

Cards

Dice		2	4	6	8	10
	1					
	2					12
	3				11	13
	4			10	12	14
	5		9	11	13	15
	6	8	10	12	14	16

[2]

b) Find the probability that Alvar will score exactly 9. Give your answer as a fraction in its simplest form.

....

[2]

[Total 4 marks]

Exam Practice Tip

When listing all the possible outcomes, it's pretty easy to either miss some out or repeat yourself — so try to go through them in a sensible way. When each outcome is equally likely, you can find the probability of something by counting how many outcomes fit what you're being asked and dividing that by the total number of outcomes.

Score

6

Section Seven — Statistics and Probability

Relative Frequency

1 Suda has a 6-sided dice. The sides are numbered 1 to 6.

Suda rolls the dice 50 times and records the results in the table below.

Number	1	2	3	4	5	6
Relative Frequency	0.32	0.12	0.24	0.14	0.06	0.12

a) How many times did she roll a 6?

....

[2]

b) Is Suda's dice fair? Explain your answer.

....

....

[2]

c) She rolls the dice another 50 times. Should she expect the same results? Explain your answer.

....

....

[1]

[Total 5 marks]

2 Cameron has a bag containing a large number of counters.
They are each numbered with a number from 1 to 5.

He selects one counter at random from the bag, records its number, and then puts it back in the bag.
Cameron does this 100 times. He records his results in the table below.

Number on counter	1	2	3	4	5
Frequency	23	25	22	21	9
Relative frequency					

a) Complete the table, giving the relative frequencies of selecting each number.

[2]

Cameron thinks there is the same number of counters with each number on in the bag.

b) Is he right? Give a reason for your answer

....

....

[1]

[Total 3 marks]

Score:

8

Section Seven — Statistics and Probability

Expected Frequency

1 The probability of a train arriving in Udderston on time is 0.64.

Hester gets the train to Udderston 200 times a year.
How many times a year can Hester expect to arrive at the station on time?

.... × 0.64 = ...

....
[Total 2 marks]

2 A bowling alley has green, purple, orange, blue and pink balls.

The probabilities that a ball chosen at random will be green, purple, orange, blue or pink are shown below.

Colour	Green	Purple	Orange	Blue	Pink
Probability	0.35	0.1	0.3	0.05	0.2

The bowling alley has 400 balls. Estimate the number of green balls.

....
[Total 2 marks]

3 Here is a 5-sided spinner.
The spinner is biased.

The probability that the spinner will land on the numbers 1 to 4 is given in this table.
I spin the spinner 100 times.

Number	1	2	3	4	5
Probability	0.3	0.15	0.2	0.25	

Estimate the number of times it will land on 5.

....
[Total 4 marks]

Exam Practice Tip

Try not to confuse expected and relative frequency. Expected frequency is the number of times you expect something to happen when you know its probability. Relative frequency is an estimate of the probability using results from an experiment.

Score

8

Section Seven — Statistics and Probability

Candidate Surname		Candidate Forename(s)	

Centre Number	Candidate Number	Candidate Signature

GCSE

Mathematics B
Paper 1 (Non-Calculator)

Foundation Tier

Practice Paper
Time allowed: 1 hour 30 minutes

You must have:
Pen, pencil, eraser, ruler, protractor, pair of compasses.
You may use tracing paper.

You are not allowed to use a calculator.

Instructions to candidates
- Use **black** ink to write your answers.
- Write your name and other details in the spaces provided above.
- Answer **all** questions in the spaces provided.
- In calculations show clearly how you worked out your answers.
- Do all rough work on the paper.

Information for candidates
- The marks available are given in brackets at the end of each question.
- You may get marks for method, even if your answer is incorrect.
- There are 26 questions in this paper. There are no blank pages.
- There are 100 marks available for this paper.
- In questions labelled with an asterisk (*), you will be assessed on the quality of your written communication — take particular care here with spelling, punctuation and the quality of explanations.

Get the answers — on video and in print
Your free Online Edition of this book includes a link to step-by-step video solutions for this Exam Paper, plus worked solutions you can print out.
There's more info about how to get your Online Edition at the front of this book.

Answer ALL the questions.

Write your answers in the spaces provided.

You must show all of your working.

1 **(a)** What is the value of the 7 in the number 13 973?

.... [1]

(b) Round the number 331 to the nearest 10

.... [1]

(c) Write out the number 1758 in words.

.... [1]

(d) Write 85.7 to the nearest whole number.

.... [1]

2 **(a)** Reflect the shaded shape in the mirror line.

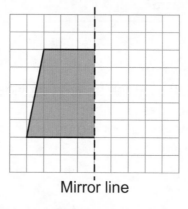

Mirror line   [1]

(b) Here is a shape with rotational symmetry.

Write down the order of rotational symmetry of this shape.

.... [1]

1

3 **(a)** Work out   7.55 × 10

.... [1]

(b) Work out   427.3 ÷ 100

.... [1]

(c) Work out   0.302 × 1000

.... [1]

4 Sam needs to buy grammar books and dictionaries for a class of students.
She needs 15 copies of each. She sees them on sale at a local book shop.

Grammar Book
£3

Dictionary
£2

(a) Calculate how much it would cost Sam to buy all the books for her class from the shop.

£ .... [2]

(b) A website sells a set of the same grammar book and dictionary together for £4.
The website has a £5 delivery charge.
Should Sam buy the books from the shop or the website? Explain your answer.

....

....

.... [2]

5 A clothes shop has 112 shirts in stock.
On Monday it sells 17 shirts, and on Tuesday morning it gets a delivery of 38 shirts.
How many shirts does it have after the delivery arrives on Tuesday?

.... [2]

2

6 Matthew surveys 20 students in his class to find out how many siblings they have. His results are shown below.

2	1	0	0	2	1	3	1	2	0
2	2	0	1	1	0	1	2	0	1

(a) Complete the table.

Number of siblings	Tally	Frequency
0		
1		
2		
3		

[2]

(b) Write down the modal number of siblings.

.... [1]

(c) Draw a bar chart on the grid below to represent Matthew's results.

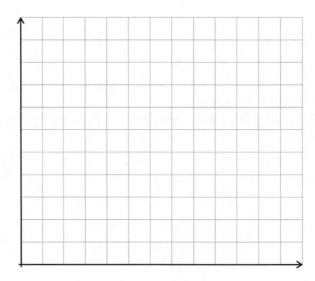

[4]

3

7 The diagram below shows a circle with centre O.

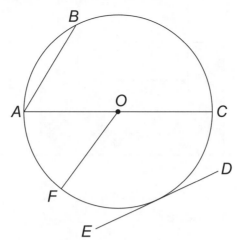

(a) Which straight line on the diagram represents the diameter of the circle?

.... *[1]*

(b) Which straight line on the diagram represents a tangent of the circle?

.... *[1]*

(c) Write down a straight line from the diagram that represents a radius of the circle.

.... *[1]*

(d) If *AC* = 10 cm, write down the length of *OF*.

.... cm *[1]*

(e) On the diagram draw a chord of the circle from point *C*.

[1]

8 The picture shows a man standing next to an elephant.

Estimate the height of the elephant.

.... m *[3]*

4

9 The shape is drawn on a grid of centimetre squares.

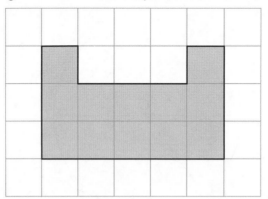

(a) What is the perimeter of the shape?

.... cm *[1]*

(b) What is the area of the shape? Make sure you give the units of your answer.

.... *[2]*

10 The table shows the temperatures in Glasgow and Barcelona at different times
on the same day.

Time	Temperature in Glasgow (°C)	Temperature in Barcelona (°C)
04 00	−8	6
08 00	−2	9
12 00	3	15
16 00	1	14
20 00	−3	11

(a) Write down the maximum temperature across the two cities.

.... °C *[1]*

(b) How much colder was Glasgow than Barcelona at 08 00?

.... °C *[2]*

(c) What was the difference between the highest temperature in Glasgow
and the lowest temperature in Barcelona?

.... °C *[3]*

5

11 Look at the triangles below.

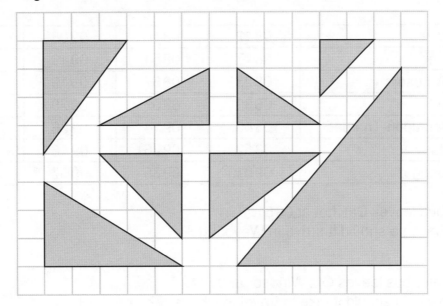

(a) Write C in the two triangles that are **congruent**.

[1]

(b) Write S in the two triangles that are **similar**.

[1]

12 Arthur thinks of three different numbers. The numbers have a range of 6 and a mean of 5.
What are the three numbers?

.............., ..., ... [2]

13 For each of the statements below, choose a number from the list which matches
the description.   19   125   36   18   84   32   124   48

(a) An even number less than 29.

.... [1]

(b) A power of 2.

.... [1]

(c) A square number.

.... [1]

(d) A cube number.

.... [1]

6

14 Below is part of a bus timetable.

Windsor	08 12	08 46	09 08	09 33
Datchet	08 17	08 51	09 13	09 38
Old Windsor	08 23	08 57	09 19	09 44
Egham	08 33	09 07	09 29	09 54
Staines-upon-Thames	08 40	09 14	09 36	10 01
Chertsey	08 52	09 26	09 48	10 13
Weybridge	09 01	09 35	09 57	10 22

(a) **(i)** A bus leaves Datchet at 08 51.
What time should it arrive in Weybridge?

....

(ii) A later bus leaves Old Windsor at 09 44.
How long should it take to travel to Chertsey?

.... minutes *[3]*

(b) Jake has a bus pass that gives him $\frac{1}{3}$ off the price of bus tickets.

He buys a return ticket from Windsor to Egham.
The normal price of the ticket is £3.60.

How much does Jake pay?

£ .... *[2]*

15 Work out the value of:
(a) 8 × 2 + 7

.... *[1]*

(b) 2³

.... *[1]*

(c) $\sqrt{49}$

.... *[1]*

*16 For work one week, Hassan drives 75 miles each day for 4 days.
He is able to claim in expenses 20p for every mile he drives.

Calculate the amount, in pounds, that he can claim in expenses for his working week.

£ .... *[3]*

17

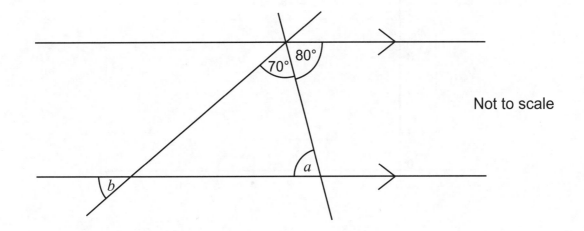

Not to scale

(a) Write down the size of angle *a* and give a reason for your answer.

....

.... *[2]*

(b) Work out the size of angle *b*.

.... ° *[2]*

8

Practice Paper 1

18 (a) Complete the table of values for $y = 2 + 2x$.

x	−1	0	1	2	3	4
y	0				8	10

[2]

(b) On the grid below, draw the graph of $y = 2 + 2x$.

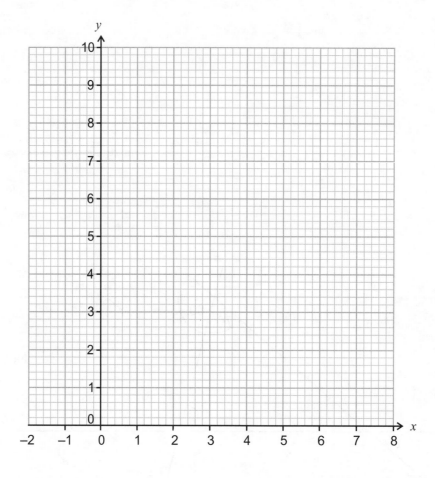

[2]

19 (a) Write down a prime number that is between 30 and 35.

.... [1]

(b) Write down all the factors of 28.

.... [2]

9

20 (a) Here are the first five terms of a number sequence.

57   46   35   24   13

(i) Write down the next number in the sequence.

....

(ii) Explain how you found your answer.

....

.... [2]

(b) The nth term of another sequence is given by $2n + 2$.
Find the 4th term of this sequence.

.... [1]

21 Here is a right-angled triangle.

50°

6 cm

Not drawn
accurately

a

8 cm

*(a) **(i)** Work out the size of angle a.

.... °

(ii) Give a reason for your answer.

.... [2]

(b) Work out the area of the triangle.

.... cm² [2]

22 (a) Solve $3x = 21$

$x =$ .... [1]

(b) Solve $2m + 5 = -9$

$m =$ .... [2]

(c) Solve $5n - 11 = 2n + 4$

$n =$ .... [2]

10

Practice Paper 1

23 Robert is the conductor of a choir that is performing a concert for charity.

Robert needs to buy sheet music for each of the 40 singers in the choir.
A website offers the sheet music for £7.00 per copy
with a 10% discount for an order of 10 or more copies.
Robert also has to pay £318 to rent the venue for the concert.

Robert sells 95 tickets for the concert. A ticket for the concert costs £10.

Robert has agreed to donate 50% of the concert profits to charity.
How much money should he donate to charity?

£ .... [7]

24 (a) Expand and simplify $3(2 + b) + 5(3 - b)$

.... [2]

(b) Factorise $6c - 8$

.... [1]

(c) Factorise fully $2d^2 + 10d$

.... [2]

11

25 A Youth Centre decides to organise a trip to a theme park.
They plan to hire a coach that costs £100 for the day.
The cost to get into the theme park is £15 per person.

The Youth Centre will charge £23 per person for the trip,
which includes the coach journey and entry to the theme park.

The trip can only go ahead if the Youth Centre makes enough money to cover its costs.
Work out how many people need to go on the trip for it to go ahead.

 [4]

26 (a) Solve the inequality $6x < 3x + 9$.

 [2]

(b) Show your solution on the number line.

[1]

Candidate Surname		Candidate Forename(s)	

Centre Number	Candidate Number	Candidate Signature

GCSE

Mathematics B
Paper 2 (Calculator)

Foundation Tier

Practice Paper
Time allowed: 1 hour 30 minutes

You must have:
Pen, pencil, eraser, ruler, protractor, pair of compasses.
You may use tracing paper.

You may use a calculator.

Instructions to candidates

- Use **black** ink to write your answers.
- Write your name and other details in the spaces provided above.
- Answer **all** questions in the spaces provided.
- In calculations show clearly how you worked out your answers.
- Do all rough work on the paper.
- Unless a question tells you otherwise, take the value of π to be 3.142, or use the π button on your calculator.

Information for candidates

- The marks available are given in brackets at the end of each question.
- You may get marks for method, even if your answer is incorrect.
- There are 26 questions in this paper. There are no blank pages.
- There are 100 marks available for this paper.
- In questions labelled with an asterisk (*), you will be assessed on the quality of your written communication — take particular care here with spelling, punctuation and the quality of explanations.

Get the answers — on video and in print

Your free Online Edition of this book includes a link to step-by-step video solutions for this Exam Paper, plus worked solutions you can print out.
There's more info about how to get your Online Edition at the front of this book.

Answer ALL the questions.

Write your answers in the spaces provided.

You must show all of your working.

1   (a) Write twenty four thousand and twelve in digits.

.... [1]

(b) Put the following numbers in order of size, from smallest to largest.

85.3   95.3   85.03   90.9   87.2

.... , ... , ... , ... , ... [1]

Jill has 4 cards, each with a number written on.

5   9   6   2

She lines all of the cards up to make a 4 digit number.

(c) (i)   What is the largest number she can make?

....

(ii) What is the smallest number she can make?

.... [2]

2   The diagram below shows a quadrilateral.

(a) Measure the length of AB.

.... cm [1]

(b) On the diagram, mark the midpoint of the line AB with a cross.

[1]

(c) Mark a right angle with the letter R.

[1]

(d) Give the mathematical name for the type of angle marked x.

.... [1]

1

3 **(a)** Write down the fraction of this shape that is shaded.

.... [1]

(b) Write down the fraction of the shape that is shaded.
Give your answer in its simplest form.

.... [2]

(c) **(i)** Shade 10% of this shape.

(ii) Write down the proportion of the shape that is **not** shaded.
Give your answer as a decimal.

.... [2]

4 **(a)** Write down the number shown by the arrow.

.... [1]

(b) Find the number 84 on the number line.
Mark it with an arrow.

[1]

2

5   The pictogram shows the number of pies eaten by customers at a restaurant one week.

Day	Number of pies eaten
Monday	
Tuesday	
Wednesday	
Thursday	
Friday	
Saturday	
Sunday	

Key: ⬤ represents 20 pies

(a) How many pies were eaten on Monday?

.... [1]

(b) How many more pies were eaten on Thursday than on Wednesday?

.... [1]

90 pies were eaten on Saturday.
35 pies were eaten on Sunday.

(c) Complete the pictogram using this information.

[2]

6   Use the words below to describe the likelihood of each of the events.

          Impossible   Unlikely   Even   Likely   Certain

(a) A card drawn at random from a pack of playing cards is a two of diamonds.

.... [1]

(b) Christmas will fall in November next year.

.... [1]

(c) When you roll a fair six-sided dice, it lands on an even number.

.... [1]

7 The table below gives some information about five candidates who have applied for a job as a postal worker.

	Driver's licence	At least grade G in GCSE Maths	Relevant work experience	Reference
Edward		✓		
Fiona	✓	✓		✓
Graham	✓		✓	✓
Nadia		✓		✓
Isaac		✓	✓	

(a) Which candidates have at least a grade G in GCSE Maths?

.... [1]

(b) Write down all the information from the table about Graham.

....

.... [1]

(c) Write down the fraction of candidates who have relevant work experience.

.... [1]

8 Complete the pattern so that it has rotational symmetry of order 4.

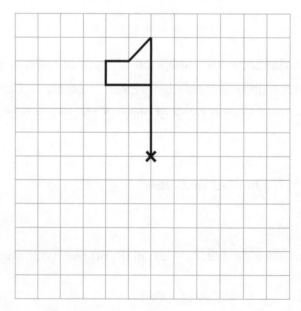

[2]

9 Draw an accurate net of the cuboid shown on the right. The first face has been drawn for you below.

Not drawn accurately

2 cm

3 cm   7 cm

[4]

10 Write down the mathematical name of each shape below.

          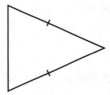

(a) ....   **(b)** ....

[2]

11 Look at the coordinate grid.

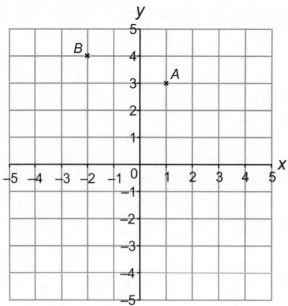

(a) Write down the coordinates of point *A*.

(...................., ...) *[1]*

(b) Write down the coordinates of point *B*.

(...................., ...) *[1]*

(c) Plot the point (−3, −4) on the grid. Label this point *C*.

[1]

12 Jemma is the manager of a shoe shop.
One week Jemma recorded the size of each pair of a particular type of shoe that was sold.

Here are her results.

6   4   7   6   4   8   4

(a) Write down the modal size sold.

.... *[1]*

(b) Work out the median size sold.

.... *[2]*

(c) Explain why Jemma might be more interested in the modal size sold than the median size.

....

.... *[1]*

6

13 Andrew runs a snack shop. These are the prices for some of the snacks he sells.

Price list

Chocolate bar	£0.70
Crisps	£0.35
Flapjack	£0.95
Cereal bar	£1.10
Apple	£0.50

(a) How much does it cost to buy a chocolate bar, a cereal bar and a flapjack?

£ .... [1]

(b) A customer buys two packets of crisps and an apple. They pay with a £5 note.
How much change should Andrew give them?

£ .... [2]

(c) Next week, Andrew is going to put all of his prices up by 20%.
How much will it cost to buy a cereal bar and an apple next week?

£ .... [3]

14 Mark is following a recipe for roasting a chicken.
The recipe gives the following information on the cooking time for a chicken:

"Cook the chicken for 50 minutes per kg, plus an extra 20 minutes."

(a) Mark has bought a chicken that weighs 2.4 kg.
Calculate how long he should cook the chicken for.

.... hours .... minutes [2]

Mark is also making a salad to go with his chicken.

Salad Dressing: Serves 4

3 tablespoons olive oil

1 tablespoon vinegar

Seasoning

(b) Mark wants to make a salad dressing for six people using the recipe above.
How much olive oil should he use?

.... tablespoons [1]

7

15 In a probability experiment, Amanda flips an ordinary coin and notes the result.
Then she rolls an ordinary unbiased 6-sided dice and notes the result.

(a) List all the possible combinations she could get.

....

.... *[2]*

Amanda flips the coin and rolls the dice.

(b) Work out the probability that Amanda gets heads on the coin **and** a 3 on the dice.

.... *[1]*

(c) Work out the probability that she gets heads on the coin **and** a 3 or higher on the dice.
Give your answer as a fraction in its simplest form.

.... *[2]*

16 Below is a scale drawing of Sharon's kitchen.

(a) The shelves are 2 m long and 0.5 m wide. What is the scale of the drawing?

1 cm to .... m *[1]*

(b) What is the area of the real kitchen?

.... m² *[3]*

17 $e = 3$, $f = 5$ and $g = -7$

Find the value of

(a) $e^2 + g^2$

.... [2]

(b) $\dfrac{efg}{2}$

.... [2]

18 The diagram shows a cuboid.

2.8 cm   Not to scale

4.9 cm   3.7 cm

(a) Calculate the volume of the cuboid. Include the correct units in your answer.

.... [3]

Another cuboid has a volume of 56 cm³, a width of 4 cm and a length of 7 cm.

(b) Calculate h, the height of the cuboid.

.... cm [2]

19 The equation $x^3 - x - 4 = 0$ has a solution between 1 and 2.

Use trial and improvement to find this solution.
Give your answer correct to one decimal place.

You must show **ALL** of your working.

$x =$ .... [4]

9

20 The graph below can be used to convert between pounds (£) and euros (€).

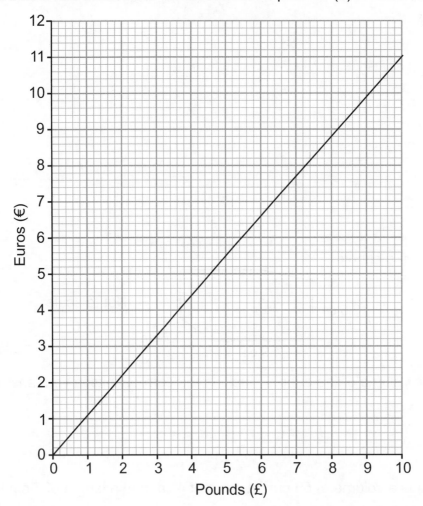

(a) Use the graph to convert £2 to euros.

€ .... *[1]*

(b) Use the graph to convert €3 to pounds.

£ .... *[1]*

(c) Use the graph to work out how much £20 is in euros.

€ .... *[2]*

21 Simplify:

(a) $a^4 \times a^5$

.... *[1]*

(b) $b^9 \div b^3$

.... *[1]*

10

22 (a) Reflect shape **A** in the line $x = 1$. Label your shape **B**.

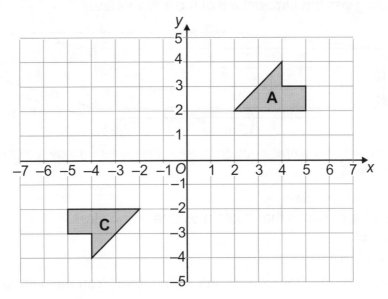

[2]

(b) Describe fully the single transformation that maps shape **C** onto shape **A**.

....

....

.... [3]

23 A large supermarket chain is planning to open a new store in Digton.
Residents of Digton are asked to complete a questionnaire to give their views on the idea.

This is one of the questions from the questionnaire.

> There is nowhere in Digton that sells a good range of products, so Digton needs a new supermarket. Do you agree?
>
> ☐ Yes   ☐ Don't know

(a) Write down one thing that is wrong with this question.

....

.... [1]

(b) Design a more suitable question that could be used instead.
Include some response boxes.

....

....

....

.... [2]

24 A painter wants to calculate the cost of painting the four outside walls of a warehouse.
The diagram below gives the dimensions of the warehouse.

3 m

15 m

12 m

Not to scale

There are 5 windows in the warehouse that each measure 2 m by 1 m and
a door that measures 3 m by 2.5 m.

The paint covers 13 m² per litre.
The paint can be bought in tins that contain 5 litres or 2.5 litres.
5 litre tins cost £20.99
2.5 litre tins cost £12.99

Calculate the cheapest price for painting the warehouse. You must show all your working.

£ .... *[6]*

25 Tom is buying nappies for his son.
He can buy nappies from two different shops.

Shop A sells medium packs that contain 32 nappies for £6.40,
Shop B sells large packs that contain 56 nappies for £7.84.

Tom has a voucher that gives him 25% off the price of nappies at shop A.

Should Tom buy the nappies at shop A or shop B?
You must show all your working.

[4]

26 (a) The diagram shows a right-angled triangle.

15.9 cm

m cm

Not to scale

12.8 cm

Calculate the value of *m*. Give your answer correct to 1 decimal place.

.... *[2]*

* **(b)** Explain why triangle *ABC* below cannot be a right-angled triangle.

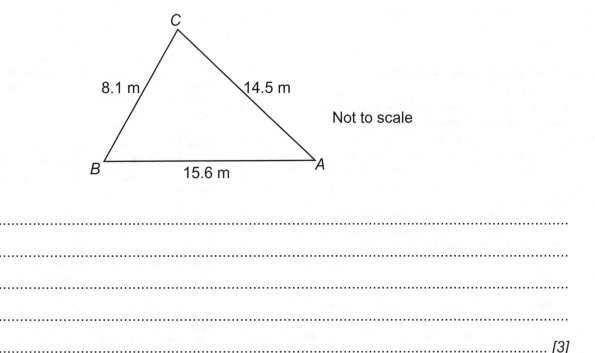

C

8.1 m 14.5 m

Not to scale

B

15.6 m

A

....

....

....

....

.... *[3]*

13

Practice Paper 2

Answers

Section One — Numbers

Pages 4-5: Ordering Numbers and Place Value

1 a) 58 *[1 mark]*
   b) 530 *[1 mark]*
   c)
   [1 mark]

2 a) Five thousand and seventy-nine *[1 mark]*
   b) 6105 *[1 mark]*
   c) 90/ninety *[1 mark]*

3 a) Twenty-six thousand and four *[1 mark]*
   b) 20 364 *[1 mark]*
   c) 800/eight hundred *[1 mark]*

4 a) Four hundred and twenty thousand, four hundred
       and fifty-seven *[1 mark]*
   b) 6 000 000 *[1 mark]*
   c) 2000/two thousand *[1 mark]*

5 98 649, 98 653, 100 003, 100 010 *[1 mark]*

6 53.3, 52.91, 35.6, 35.54, 35.06 *[1 mark]*

7 a) 12 478 *[1 mark]*
   b) 87 421 *[1 mark]*

Pages 6-7: Addition and Subtraction

1 522 − 197 = 325
   *[2 marks available — 1 mark for a correct method of subtraction,
   1 mark for the correct answer]*

2 £290 + £59 + £39 + £95 = £483
   *[3 marks available — 1 mark for finding the correct costs,
   1 mark for adding them together, 1 mark for the correct answer]*

3 £15 − £8.50 + £20 − £18 = £8.50, so he would not have
   £10 to give to his sister.
   *[2 marks available — 1 mark for adding and subtracting the
   correct amounts to work out how much he would have left,
   1 mark for the correct conclusion]*

4 Total cost = £2.15 + £2.40 + £2.40 = £6.95
   Change = £10 − £6.95 = £3.05
   *[2 marks available — 1 mark for adding amounts and
   subtracting from £10, 1 mark for the correct answer]*

5 a) E.g. Toast (2 slices) and coffee, or yoghurt with fruit and tea.
       *[2 marks available — 2 marks for 2 correct combinations
       and no incorrect combinations, otherwise 1 mark for
       1 correct combination]*
       *Parvati could also buy toast (2 slices) and tea or
       toast (2 slices) and fresh orange juice.*
   b) £3.40 + £2.30 + £1.40 + £1.50 = £8.60
       £10 − £8.60 = £1.40
       *[3 marks available — 1 mark for finding the correct costs,
       1 mark for adding them together and subtracting from £10,
       1 mark for the correct answer]*

Page 8: Multiplying and Dividing by 10, 100, etc.

1 a) 32.8 × 10 = 328 *[1 mark]*
   b) 429 ÷ 10 = 42.9 *[1 mark]*
   c) 22.2 × 1000 = 22 200 *[1 mark]*

2 a) 4.268 × 100 = 426.8 *[1 mark]*
   b) 304 ÷ 100 = 3.04 *[1 mark]*
   c) 2470 ÷ 1000 = 2.47 *[1 mark]*

3 a) 23 × **1000** = 23 000 *[1 mark]*
   b) 46 000 ÷ **100** = 460 *[1 mark]*

Pages 9-10: Multiplying and Dividing Without a Calculator

1
$$\begin{array}{r} 113 \\ \times\ \ 76 \\ \hline 678 \\ +\ 7910 \\ \hline 8588 \end{array}$$
   *[2 marks available — 1 mark for a correct method,
   1 mark for the correct answer]*
   *"A correct method" here can be any non-calculator
   multiplication method.*

2 a) 19 + 26 ÷ 2 = 19 + 13 = 32
       *[2 marks available — 1 mark for doing the calculation
       steps in the correct order, 1 mark for the correct answer]*
   b) (22 − 18) × (3 + 8) = 4 × 11 = 44
       *[2 marks available — 1 mark for doing the calculation
       steps in the correct order, 1 mark for the correct answer]*

3 (9 − 3) × 2 + 2 = 14 *[1 mark]*

4 Total miles travelled = (30 × 2) + (28 × 2) + (39 × 2) + (40 × 2)
                         = 60 + 56 + 78 + 80
                         = 274 miles
   Expenses for miles travelled = 274 × 30p = 8220p = £82.20
   Expenses for food = 4 × £8 = £32
   Total expenses = £82.20 + £32 = £114.20
   *[5 marks available — 1 mark for multiplying the distances by 2,
   1 mark for finding total miles, 1 mark for multiplying total
   miles by 30 or 0.3(0), 1 mark for finding food expenses,
   1 mark for the correct final answer]*

5 £200 − £5 = £195
   $\begin{array}{r} 13 \\ 15\overline{)19^4 5} \end{array}$, so each ticket costs £13
   *[3 marks available — 1 mark for subtracting £5 from £200,
   1 mark for dividing £195 by 15, 1 mark for the correct
   final answer]*

6 Slices of pizza he needs = 15 × 3 = 45 *[1 mark]*
   Number of pizzas he needs = 45 ÷ 8 *[1 mark]*
                             = 5.625
   So he needs 6 pizzas *[1 mark]*
   A 300 g packet of crisps is enough for 300 ÷ 25 = 12 people *[1 mark]*
   So James needs 2 packets of crisps *[1 mark]*
   [5 marks available in total — as above]

7 Fresh water: (9300 ÷ 100) × 12p = 93 × 12p = 1116p = £11.16
   Waste water disposal: (8600 ÷ 100) × 9p = 86 × 9p = 774p = £7.74
   Total water bill = £11.16 + £7.74 + £7 = £25.90
   *[6 marks available — 1 mark for dividing 9300 or 8600 by 100,
   1 mark for multiplying 93 by 12p, 1 mark for multiplying 86 by 9p,
   1 mark for £11.16, 1 mark for £7.74 and 1 mark for the correct
   final answer]*

Page 11: Multiplying and Dividing with Decimals

1 a)
$$\begin{array}{r} 16 \\ \times\ \ 7 \\ \hline 112 \end{array}$$
       16 × 0.7 has one digit after the decimal point,
       so 16 × 0.7 = 11.2
       *[2 marks available — 1 mark for the correct digits in the right
       order, 1 mark for the correct position of the decimal point]*
       "A correct method" can be any non-calculator multiplication method.
   b)
$$\begin{array}{r} 25 \\ \times\ \ 19 \\ \hline 225 \\ +\ 250 \\ \hline 475 \end{array}$$
       2.5 × 1.9 has two digits after the decimal point,
       so 2.5 × 1.9 = 4.75
       *[2 marks available — 1 mark for a correct method,
       1 mark for the correct answer]*

2 a) $5.6 \times 4.27 = (23\ 912 \div 10) \div 100 = 23.912$ *[1 mark]*

b) $0.56 \times 4\ 270\ 000 = (23\ 912 \div 100) \times 10\ 000 = 2\ 391\ 200$
[1 mark]

c) $2391.2 \div 4.27 = (56 \div 10) \times 100 = 560$ *[1 mark]*

3 $7 \times 8 = 56$
0.7×0.8 has two digits after the decimal point,
so $0.7 \times 0.8 = 0.56$
[2 marks available — 1 mark for a correct method,
1 mark for the correct answer]

4 a) $14 \div 0.7 = \dfrac{14}{0.7} = \dfrac{140}{7} = 20$

[2 marks available — 1 mark for a correct method,
1 mark for the correct answer]

b) $23 \div 0.46 = \dfrac{23}{0.46} = \dfrac{2300}{46} = 50$

[2 marks available — 1 mark for a correct method,
1 mark for the correct answer]

Page 12: Negative Numbers

1 $-103.1, -102.7, -102.4, -99.8, -98.9, 98.9, 99.5$ *[1 mark]*

2 a) $9 - 4 = 5\ °C$ *[1 mark]*

b) St Petersburg *[1 mark]*

c) $22 - (-8) = 30\ °C$
[3 marks available — 1 mark for finding the correct values,
1 mark for subtracting, 1 mark for the correct answer]

3 a) $-11 \times 7 = -77$ *[1 mark]*

b) $-72 \div -8 = 9$ *[1 mark]*

Page 13: Special Types of Number

1 a) 41 *[1 mark]*

b) 100 *[1 mark]*

c) 27 *[1 mark]*

2 a) 81 *[1 mark]*

b) 64 *[1 mark]*

c) 6 *[1 mark]*

Page 14: Prime Numbers, Multiples and Factors

1 a) 7 or 11 *[1 mark for either]*

b) 15 *[1 mark]*

c) 15 *[1 mark]*

d) 1 and 12, or 7 and 12, or 11 and 12
[1 mark available — 1 mark maximum for any of the three
options above]

2 a) 1, 2, 4, 5, 10, 20
[2 marks available — 2 marks if all 6 factors are correct
and no extra incorrect factors have been included,
otherwise 1 mark if all 6 factors are correct but 1 extra
incorrect factor has been included, or if at least 4 factors are
correct and there are no more than 6 numbers listed in total]

b) 56, 64 *[1 mark]*

3 a) E.g. 21, 42 *[1 mark for any two multiples of 21]*

b) 47 *[1 mark]*

Page 15: Prime Factors, LCM and HCF

1 a)

$72 = 2 \times 2 \times 2 \times 3 \times 3$
[2 marks available — 1 mark for a correct method,
1 mark for all prime factors correct]

b) Factors of 54 are: 1, 2, 3, 6, 9, (18), 27, 54
Factors of 72 are: 1, 2, 3, 4, 6, 8, 9, 12, (18), 24, 36, 72

So the highest common factor (HCF) is 18 *[1 mark]*
You could use the prime factors to go straight to finding
the HCF, but there's a good chance of making a mistake.
It's much safer to list all the factors and find the HCF
that way, even if it takes a bit longer.

2 Multiples of 3 are: 3, 6, 9, 12, (15), 18, ...
Multiples of 5 are: 5, 10, (15), 20, ...

So it will be 15 minutes until they are side by side at the start line.
[2 marks available — 1 mark for a correct method,
1 mark for the correct answer]

3 Multiples of 35 are: 35, 70, 105, 140, 175, 210, 245, 280, 315, 350,
(385), 420, ...
Multiples of 55 are: 55, 110, 165, 220, 275, 330, (385), 440, ...

So the LCM is 385, which is the minimum number of jars he needs.

So the minimum number of packs he needs is $385 \div 35 = 11$ packs
[3 marks available — 1 mark for a correct method to find LCM,
1 mark for LCM correct, 1 mark for correct number of packs]

Page 16: Fractions, Decimals and Percentages

1 a) $\dfrac{3}{4} = 3 \div 4 = 0.75$ *[1 mark]*

b) $0.06 \times 100 = 6\%$ *[1 mark]*

c) $35\% = \dfrac{35}{100}$ *[1 mark]*

$= \dfrac{35 \div 5}{100 \div 5} = \dfrac{7}{20}$ *[1 mark]*
[2 marks available in total — as above]

2 a) $14 \div 20 = 0.7$ *[1 mark]*

$0.7 \times 100 = 70\%$ *[1 mark]*
[2 marks available in total — as above]
Or you could multiply the top and bottom of the fraction by 5 to

give $\dfrac{70}{100} = 70\%$.

b) $85\% = \dfrac{85}{100}$ *[1 mark]*

$= \dfrac{85 \div 5}{100 \div 5} = \dfrac{17}{20}$ *[1 mark]*

[2 marks available in total — as above]

3 $\dfrac{3}{5}, 0.65, 80\%$
[2 marks available — 2 marks for the correct final answer,
otherwise 1 mark if numbers in reverse order or one value is in the
correct place]
You could convert all the values to the same type of number (fractions,
decimals or percentages), to find out which order they should go in.

Page 17: Equivalent Fractions

1 a) $\dfrac{12 \div 6}{30 \div 6} = \dfrac{2}{5}$ *[1 mark]*

b) 18 shaded squares out of 50, so $\dfrac{18}{50} = \dfrac{9}{25}$
[2 marks available — 2 marks for the correct final answer,
otherwise 1 mark for a correct equivalent fraction]

c) E.g.

[1 mark for any 40 squares shaded]

2 a) $\dfrac{18}{7} = 2\dfrac{4}{7}$ *[1 mark]*

b) $1\dfrac{3}{4} = \dfrac{4 + 3}{4} = \dfrac{7}{4}$ *[1 mark]*

3 a) $\dfrac{3}{12} = \dfrac{1}{4} \neq \dfrac{1}{3}$ and $\dfrac{6}{20} = \dfrac{3}{10} \neq \dfrac{3}{9} = \dfrac{1}{3}$
So $\dfrac{3}{12}$ and $\dfrac{6}{20}$
[2 marks available — 1 mark for each correct answer]

b) $\frac{4}{5} = \frac{36}{45}$, $\frac{7}{9} = \frac{35}{45}$, $\frac{13}{15} = \frac{39}{45}$

So the largest fraction is $\frac{13}{15}$

[3 marks available — 1 mark for attempting to convert to equivalent fractions or to draw shaded diagrams, 1 mark if these are correct, 1 mark for the correct conclusion]

Pages 18-20: Fractions

1 a) $\frac{1}{2} \times \frac{1}{6} = \frac{1 \times 1}{2 \times 6} = \frac{1}{12}$ *[1 mark]*

b) $\frac{2}{3} \div \frac{3}{5} = \frac{2}{3} \times \frac{5}{3} = \frac{2 \times 5}{3 \times 3} = \frac{10}{9}$ or $1\frac{1}{9}$

[2 marks available — 1 mark for changing to the reciprocal fraction and multiplying, 1 mark for the correct answer]

2 a) $\frac{3}{4} \times \frac{2}{5} = \frac{3 \times 2}{4 \times 5} = \frac{6}{20} = \frac{3}{10}$

[2 marks available — 1 mark for multiplying the fractions, 1 mark for the final answer in its simplest form]

b) $9 \overline{)2.^2 0^2 0^2 0...}$ $0.2\ 2\ 2...$

So $\frac{2}{9} = 0.222... = 0.\dot{2}$

[3 marks available — 1 mark for using a division method, 1 mark for 0.22..., 1 mark for the correct final answer]

3 a) $\frac{1}{6} + \frac{2}{3} = \frac{1}{6} + \frac{4}{6} = \frac{1+4}{6} = \frac{5}{6}$

[2 marks available — 1 mark for finding a common denominator, 1 mark for the correct answer]

b) $\frac{7}{8} - \frac{3}{4} = \frac{7}{8} - \frac{6}{8} = \frac{7-6}{8} = \frac{1}{8}$

[2 marks available — 1 mark for finding a common denominator, 1 mark for the correct answer]

4 a) $\frac{1}{3} + \frac{2}{5} = \frac{5}{15} + \frac{6}{15} = \frac{5+6}{15} = \frac{11}{15}$

[2 marks available — 1 mark for finding a common denominator, 1 mark for the correct answer]

b) $\frac{1}{2} - \frac{2}{7} = \frac{7}{14} - \frac{4}{14} = \frac{7-4}{14} = \frac{3}{14}$

[2 marks available — 1 mark for finding a common denominator, 1 mark for the correct answer]

5 a) $(60 \div 5) \times 3 = 12 \times 3 = 36$

[2 marks available — 1 mark for dividing by 5, 1 mark for the correct answer]

You could also multiply 60 by 0.6.

b) $\frac{15}{40} = \frac{3}{8}$

[2 marks available — 1 mark for putting the numbers into a fraction, 1 mark for the correct final answer]

6 $(12\ 400 \div 8) \times 3 = 1550 \times 3 = 4650$

[2 marks available — 1 mark for dividing by 8, 1 mark for the correct answer]

7 $1 - \frac{7}{10} = \frac{3}{10}$

$(£79 \div 10) \times 3 = £7.90 \times 3 = £23.70$

[3 marks available — 1 mark for finding the fraction to spend on fiction books, 1 mark for dividing by 10, 1 mark for the correct answer]

8 $12 \times \frac{2}{5} = \frac{24}{5}$ *[1 mark]*

$\frac{24}{5} = 4\frac{4}{5}$ *[1 mark]*

Sarah will need to order 5 pizzas. *[1 mark]*

[3 marks available in total — as above]

Remember to round up — 4 pizzas wouldn't be enough.

9 Calculate the total cost if he pays in full today:

$£1100 \div 4 = £275$, $£1100 - £275 = £825$

Calculate the total cost if he pays £150 today, then 12 monthly payments of £55:

$£150 + (12 \times £55) = £150 + £660 = £810$

So the cheaper way for Chris to pay for the car is by paying £150 today, followed by 12 monthly payments of £55.

[4 marks available — 1 mark for the correct method to find the total cost if he pays in full today, 1 mark for the correct method

to find the total cost if he pays £150 then 12 monthly payments, 1 mark if both of these values are correct, 1 mark for the correct conclusion from your values]

10 7 *[1 mark]*

11 $0.0\dot{9}$ *[1 mark]*

12 $\frac{1}{7}$ *[1 mark]*

Page 21: Proportion Problems

1 Price per ml:

250 ml bottle: $£2.30 \div 250 = £0.0092$

330 ml bottle: $£2.97 \div 330 = £0.009$

500 ml bottle: $£4.10 \div 500 = £0.0082$

Therefore the 500 ml bottle is the best value for money.

[2 marks available — 1 mark for finding the price per ml, 1 mark for the correct answer]

2 Flour: $(175 \div 20) \times 70 = 612.5$ g

Butter: $(175 \div 20) \times 70 = 612.5$ g

Sugar: $(120 \div 20) \times 70 = 420$ g

Baking powder: $(2.5 \div 20) \times 70 = 8.75$ tsp

Eggs: $(4 \div 20) \times 70 = 14$

[3 marks available — 1 mark for dividing each quantity by 20, 1 mark for multiplying each of these by 70, 1 mark if all 5 final answers are correct]

Page 22: Percentages

1 $100\% = £450$

$10\% = £450 \div 10 = £45$

$60\% = £45 \times 6 = £270$

[2 marks available — 1 mark for a correct method, 1 mark for the correct final answer]

2 $50 - 35 = 15$, so 15 of the pigs are male. *[1 mark]*

$\frac{15}{50} \times 100$ *[1 mark]*

$= 30\%$ *[1 mark]*

[3 marks available in total — as above]

3 a) $10\% = 10 \div 100 = 0.1$

10% of $£18 = 0.1 \times £18 = £1.80$

[2 marks available — 1 mark for a correct method, 1 mark for the correct answer]

b) $(£6 \div £24) \times 100 = 0.25 \times 100 = 25\%$

[2 marks available — 1 mark for a correct method, 1 mark for the correct answer]

4 $20\% = 20 \div 100 = 0.2$

20% of $£33.25 = 0.2 \times £33.25 = £6.65$

$£33.25 + £6.65 = £39.90$

[3 marks available — 1 mark for a correct method to find 20% of £33.25, 1 mark for adding this to £33.25, 1 mark for the correct answer]

You could multiply by 1.2 instead of multiplying by 0.2 and adding.

Pages 23-24: Ratios

1 $\div 4 \binom{4:12}{1:3} \div 4$

[1 mark]

2 a) boys : girls

$= 12 : 14$

$= 6 : 7$ *[1 mark]*

b) $25 \div (2 + 3) = 5$ *[1 mark]*

Number of girls is $5 \times 3 = 15$ *[1 mark]*

[2 marks available in total — as above]

3 $700 \div (4 + 3 + 7) = 700 \div 14$

$= 50$ ml

Orange juice: $50 \times 4 = 200$ ml

Pineapple juice : $50 \times 3 = 150$ ml

Lemonade: $50 \times 7 = 350$ ml

[3 marks available — 1 mark for dividing 700 by the sum of the numbers in the ratio, 1 mark for multiplying this number by each number in the ratio, 1 mark if all three quantities are correct]

4 £160 ÷ (3 + 6 + 7) = £160 ÷ 16 *[1 mark]*
                     = £10
  So Christine's share = £10 × 7 = £70 *[1 mark]*
  [2 marks available in total — as above]

5 360 ÷ 9 *[1 mark]*
  = 40
  40 × 7 = 280 *[1 mark]*
  360 + 280 = 640 *[1 mark]*
  [3 marks available in total — as above]

6 a) E.g. Hannah is wrong because there could be 8 apple trees and 10 cherry trees. *[1 mark]*
    b) 4 + 5 = 9
       126 ÷ 9 = 14 *[1 mark]*
       14 × 4 = 56 apple trees *[1 mark]*
       14 × 5 = 70 cherry trees *[1 mark]*
       [3 marks available in total — as above]

Page 25: Rounding Off and Estimating Calculations

1 a) 120 *[1 mark]*
    b) 2600 *[1 mark]*
    c) 500 000 *[1 mark]*
    d) 428.6 light years *[1 mark]*

2 $\dfrac{4.32^2 - \sqrt{13.4}}{16.3 + 2.19}$ = 0.8113466... *[1 mark]*
                 = 0.811 *[1 mark]*
  [2 marks available in total — as above]

3 a) E.g. $\dfrac{3.2 \times 398.4}{1.87^2} \approx \dfrac{3 \times 400}{2^2} = \dfrac{1200}{4} = 300$
      [2 marks available — 1 mark for rounding to suitable values, 1 mark for the correct final answer using your values]
    b) E.g. 1720 × 11.3 ≈ 2000 × 10 = 20 000p
      20 000 ÷ 100 = £200
      No, Mr Potts is not correct.
      [3 marks available — 1 mark for rounding to suitable values, 1 mark for converting cost into pounds, 1 mark for the correct concluding statement]

Page 26: Powers and Roots

1 a) 8.7^3 = 658.503 *[1 mark]*
    b) $\sqrt{2025}$ = 45 *[1 mark]*

2 Since 6^2 = 36 and 7^2 = 49, 6 < $\sqrt{42}$ < 7
  So, $\sqrt{42} \approx 6.5$ *[1 mark]*
  You would be given the mark here for any answer which was greater than 6 and less than 7.

3 a) $6^{(4+7)}$ = 6^{11} *[1 mark]*
    b) $6^{(5-3)}$ = 6^2 *[1 mark]*

4 $\dfrac{3^4 \times 3^7}{3^6} = \dfrac{3^{(4+7)}}{3^6} = \dfrac{3^{11}}{3^6} = 3^{(11-6)} = 3^5$
  [2 marks available — 1 mark for a correct attempt at adding or subtracting powers, 1 mark for the correct final answer]

Section Two — Algebra

Page 27: Simplifying Terms

1 a) 4p *[1 mark]*
    b) 2m *[1 mark]*
    c) 4p + 3r
      [2 marks available — 1 mark for 4p and 1 mark for 3r]

2 a) w^5 *[1 mark]*
    b) $x^{(9-3)} = x^6$ *[1 mark]*
    c) y^5 *[1 mark]*
      Remember — if you're multiplying, you add the powers.

3 a) 10ab *[1 mark]*
    b) 4pq *[1 mark]*
    c) $x^2 + 4x$
      [2 marks available — 1 mark for x^2 and 1 mark for 4x]

Page 28: Multiplying Out Brackets

1 a) 3(x − 2)
      = (3 × x) + (3 × −2)
      = 3x − 6 *[1 mark]*
    b) x(x + 4)
      = (x × x) + (x × 4)
      = $x^2 + 4x$ *[1 mark]*

2 a) 5(x + y)
      = (5 × x) + (5 × y)
      = 5x + 5y *[1 mark]*
    b) s(2s − 3)
      = (s × 2s) + (s × −3)
      = $2s^2 − 3s$ *[1 mark]*
    c) 2a(2a + 3)
      = (2a × 2a) + (2a × 3)
      = $4a^2 + 6a$ *[1 mark]*
    d) 2b − 3(b − 1)
      = 2b + (−3 × b) + (−3 × −1)
      = 2b − 3b + 3 *[1 mark]*
      = 3 − b *[1 mark]*
      [2 marks available in total — as above]

3 a) 3(x − 1) + 5(x + 2)
      = (3 × x) + (3 × −1) + (5 × x) + (5 × 2)
      = 3x − 3 + 5x + 10 *[1 mark]*
      = 8x + 7 *[1 mark]*
      [2 marks available in total — as above]
    b) 4a(a + 2b)
      = (4a × a) + (4a × 2b)
      = $4a^2 + 8ab$ *[1 mark]*
    c) 9 − 3(x + 2)
      = 9 + (−3 × x) + (−3 × 2)
      = 9 − 3x − 6 *[1 mark]*
      = 3 − 3x *[1 mark]*
      [2 marks available in total — as above]

Page 29: Taking Out Common Factors

1 a) 6x + 3 = (3 × 2x) + (3 × 1) = 3(2x + 1) *[1 mark]*
    b) x(x + 7) *[1 mark]*
    c) 5(5p − 3q) *[1 mark]*

2 $4a^2 − 24ab = 4(a^2 − 6ab)$
               = 4a(a − 6b)
  [2 marks available — 2 marks for the correct final answer, otherwise 1 mark if the expression is only partly factorised]

3 a) $7y − 21y^2 = 7(y − 3y^2)$
              = 7y(1 − 3y)
      [2 marks available — 2 marks for the correct final answer, otherwise 1 mark if the expression is only partly factorised]
    b) $18t + 9t^2 = 9(2t + t^2)$
             = 9t(2 + t)
      [2 marks available — 2 marks for the correct final answer, otherwise 1 mark if the expression is only partly factorised]

4 a) $4x^2 + 6xy = 2(2x^2 + 3xy)$
              = 2x(2x + 3y)
      [2 marks available — 2 marks for the correct final answer, otherwise 1 mark if the expression is only partly factorised]
    b) $2vw + 8v^2 = 2(vw + 4v^2)$
             = 2v(w + 4v)
      [2 marks available — 2 marks for the correct final answer, otherwise 1 mark if the expression is only partly factorised]

Pages 30-31: Solving Equations

1 a) x + 3 = 12
      x = 12 − 3 = 9 *[1 mark]*
    b) 6x = 24
      x = 24 ÷ 6 = 4 *[1 mark]*

134

2 a) $p - 11 = -7$
         $p = -7 + 11 = 4$ *[1 mark]*
  b) $2y - 5 = 9$
         $2y = 9 + 5 = 14$ *[1 mark]*
         $y = 14 \div 2 = 7$ *[1 mark]*
         [2 marks available in total — as above]
  c) $3z + 2 = z + 15$
         $3z - z = 15 - 2$
         $2z = 13$ *[1 mark]*
         $z = 13 \div 2 = 6.5$ *[1 mark]*
         [2 marks available in total — as above]

3 a) $3x + 5 = 14$
         $3x = 14 - 5 = 9$ *[1 mark]*
         $x = 9 \div 3 = 3$ *[1 mark]*
         [2 marks available in total — as above]
  b) $7x - 4 = 2x + 1$
         $7x - 2x = 1 + 4$
         $5x = 5$ *[1 mark]*
         $x = 5 \div 5 = 1$ *[1 mark]*
         [2 marks available in total — as above]

4 a) $40 - 3x = 17x$
         $40 = 17x + 3x$
         $40 = 20x$ *[1 mark]*
         $x = 40 \div 20 = 2$ *[1 mark]*
         [2 marks available in total — as above]
  b) $2y - 5 = 3y - 12$
         $-5 + 12 = 3y - 2y$ *[1 mark]*
         $y = 7$ *[1 mark]*
         [2 marks available in total — as above]

5 a) $3(a + 2) = 15$
         $(3 \times a) + (3 \times 2) = 15$
         $3a + 6 = 15$ *[1 mark]*
         $3a = 15 - 6$
         $3a = 9$ *[1 mark]*
         $a = 9 \div 3 = 3$ *[1 mark]*
         [3 marks available in total — as above]
  b) $2b - 6 = 2(3b + 1)$
         $2b - 6 = 6b + 2$ *[1 mark]*
         $-6 - 2 = 6b - 2b$
         $-8 = 4b$ *[1 mark]*
         $b = -8 \div 4 = -2$ *[1 mark]*
         [3 marks available in total — as above]

6 a) $9(e - 2) = 3e + 6$
         $9e - 18 = 3e + 6$ *[1 mark]*
         $9e - 3e = 6 + 18$
         $6e = 24$ *[1 mark]*
         $e = 24 \div 6 = 4$ *[1 mark]*
         [3 marks available in total — as above]
  b) $5(2c - 1) = 4(3c - 2)$
         $10c - 5 = 12c - 8$ *[1 mark]*
         $-5 + 8 = 12c - 10c$
         $3 = 2c$ *[1 mark]*
         $c = 3 \div 2 = 1.5$ *[1 mark]*
         [3 marks available in total — as above]

Page 32: Writing Equations

1 $7x - 12 = 4x$ *[1 mark]*
   $3x = 12$
   $x = 4$
   So Alexa's original number was 4. *[1 mark]*
   [2 marks available in total — as above]

2 Perimeter of ABC = perimeter of $EFGH$
   $3(x + 4) = 2(2x + 4) + 2(x - 1)$ *[1 mark]*
   $(3 \times x) + (3 \times 4) = (2 \times 2x) + (2 \times 4) + (2 \times x) + (2 \times -1)$
   $3x + 12 = 4x + 8 + 2x - 2$ *[1 mark]*
   $3x + 12 = 6x + 6$
   $3x = 6$ *[1 mark]*
   $x = 2$ *[1 mark]*
   [4 marks available in total — as above]

3 $(x + 15°) + (x + 60°) + 3x = 180°$ *[1 mark]*
   $5x + 75° = 180°$ *[1 mark]*
   $5x = 105°$
   $x = 21°$ *[1 mark]*
   Therefore largest angle = $x + 60° = 81°$ *[1 mark]*
   [4 marks available in total — as above]

Page 33: Using Formulas

1 $Q = 7x - 3y$
   $Q = (7 \times 8) - (3 \times 7)$
   $Q = 56 - 21 = 35$
   [2 marks available — 1 mark for correct substitution of x and y, 1 mark for correct final answer]

2 $S = 4m^2 + 2.5n$
   $S = (4 \times 6.5 \times 6.5) + (2.5 \times 4)$
   $S = 169 + 10$
   $S = 179$
   [2 marks available — 1 mark for correct substitution of m and n, 1 mark for correct final answer]

3 $F = \dfrac{9C}{5} + 32$
   $F = (9 \times 35 \div 5) + 32$
   $F = 95 \ °F$
   [2 marks available — 1 mark for correct substitution of C, 1 mark for correct final answer]

4 a) $C = S + 7H$
         $C = 25 + (7 \times 13)$
         $C = 25 + 91 = 116$
         The cost will be £116.
         [2 marks available — 1 mark for correct substitution of S and H, 1 mark for correct final answer]
  b) $C = 2H + 5N$
         $C = (2 \times 3) + (5 \times 5)$
         $C = 6 + 25 = 31$
         The cost would be £31.
         [2 marks available — 1 mark for correct substitution of H and N, 1 mark for correct final answer]

Pages 34-35: Writing and Rearranging Formulas

1 a) Total cost = flat fee + (cost per day × number of days)
         $C = 300 + (50 \times d)$
         $C = 300 + 50d$
         [2 marks available — 2 marks for correct formula, otherwise 1 mark for just 300 + 50d]
  b) Substitute $d = 3$ into formula:
         $C = 300 + (50 \times 3)$
         $C = 300 + 150 = 450$
         Therefore Alex would have to pay £450.
         [2 marks available — 1 mark for substitution of d = 3 into formula, 1 mark for correct final answer]

2 a) Number of miles = (number of kilometres ÷ 8) × 5
         $m = (k \div 8) \times 5$
         $m = \dfrac{5k}{8}$
         [2 marks available — 2 marks for correct formula, otherwise 1 mark for just $\frac{5k}{8}$]
  b) Substitute $k = 110$ into formula:
         $m = \dfrac{5 \times 110}{8}$
         $m = 550 \div 8 = 68.75$
         Therefore 110 km = 68.75 miles.
         [2 marks available — 1 mark for substitution of k = 110 into formula, 1 mark for correct final answer]

3 a) $v + m$ *[1 mark]*
  b) Thickness of a book in mm =
         (thickness of 1 cover in mm × number of covers) +
         (thickness of 1 page in mm × number of pages)
         $t = (3 \times 2) + (0.1 \times x)$
         $t = 6 + 0.1x$
         [2 marks available — 2 marks for correct formula, otherwise 1 mark for just 6 + 0.1x]

Answers

4 a) Total cost = flat fee + (number of pieces of furniture × cost per piece of furniture)
$A = 35 + (F \times 10)$
$A = 35 + 10F$
[2 marks available — 2 marks for correct formula, otherwise 1 mark for just 35 + 10F]

b) Rearrange formula to give F in terms of A.
$A - 35 = 10F$
$F = \dfrac{A - 35}{10}$
Substitute $A = 105$ into new formula to find F:
$F = (105 - 35) \div 10 = 7$
Therefore 7 pieces of furniture are being delivered.
[3 marks available — 1 mark for rearranging the formula, 1 mark for substituting A = 105 into the formula, 1 mark for the correct final answer]

5 $P = (2x) + (2x + 1) + (3x - 5) + (2x + 1) + (2x) + (4x + 3)$
$\qquad + ((2x) + (3x - 5) + (2x)) + (4x + 3)$
$P = 26x - 2$
[3 marks available — 1 mark for identifying the 2 missing sides, 1 mark for adding together all the side lengths, 1 mark for simplifying the expression]
The vertical side on the far left is the same as the one on the far right, and the length of the bottom of the shape is just the three shorter horizontal sides at the top added together.

6 a) $u = v - at$ *[1 mark]*
b) $v - u = at$ *[1 mark]*
$t = \dfrac{v - u}{a}$ *[1 mark]*
[2 marks available in total — as above]

Pages 36-37: Number Patterns and Sequences

1 a) 36, 44 *[1 mark]*
b) 23rd term = 25th term − (2 × difference between terms)
$= 196 - (2 \times 8) = 196 - 16 = 180$ *[1 mark]*
c) All of the terms in the sequence must be a multiple of 4 (the first term is 4, and the difference between the terms is 8). *[1 mark]*
90 isn't a multiple of 4, so it can't be the 12th term. *[1 mark]*
[2 marks available in total — as above]
You could also work out the 12th term and show that it's not 90.

2 a) 8, 13, 18, 23, 28, 33, 38
Rule: add 5 each time.
[2 marks available — 1 mark for all correct terms, 1 mark for the correct rule]
b) 3, 6, 12, 24, 48, 96
Rule: double the previous number each time.
[2 marks available — 1 mark for all correct terms, 1 mark for the correct rule]

3 a)
[1 mark]
b) 81, because the number of triangles in the nth pattern is equal to n^2.
[2 marks available — 1 mark for 81 and 1 mark for the correct reason]

4 a) $1^2 + 4 = 5$ *[1 mark]*
b) $8^2 + 4 = 68$ *[1 mark]*

5 a)
2   9   16   23
$\quad$ +7 +7 +7
The common difference is 7, so $7n$ is in the formula.
$n = 1 \quad 2 \quad 3 \quad 4$
$7n = 7 \quad 14 \quad 21 \quad 28$
$\quad \downarrow{-5} \downarrow{-5} \downarrow{-5} \downarrow{-5}$
nth term = 2 $\quad$ 9 $\quad$ 16 $\quad$ 23
You have to subtract 5 to get to the term.
So the expression for the nth term is $7n - 5$.
[2 marks available — 2 marks for the correct expression, otherwise 1 mark for 7n]

b) 30th term = $(7 \times 30) - 5 = 205$ *[1 mark]*

6 3 $\quad$ 7 $\quad$ 11 $\quad$ 15 $\quad$ 19
$\quad$ +4 $\quad$ +4 $\quad$ +4 $\quad$ +4
The common difference is 4, so $4n$ is in the formula.
$4n = 4 \quad 8 \quad 12 \quad 16 \quad 20$
$\quad \downarrow{-1} \downarrow{-1} \downarrow{-1} \downarrow{-1} \downarrow{-1}$
nth term = 3 $\quad$ 7 $\quad$ 11 $\quad$ 15 $\quad$ 19
You have to subtract 1 to get to the term.
So the expression for the nth term is $4n - 1$.
[2 marks available — 2 marks for the correct expression, otherwise 1 mark for 4n]

Page 38: Trial and Improvement

1

x	$x^3 + 4x$	
2	$2^3 + (4 \times 2) = 8 + 8 = 16$	Too small
3	$3^3 + (4 \times 3) = 27 + 12 = 39$	Too big
2.5	$2.5^3 + (4 \times 2.5) = 25.625$	Too big
2.3	$2.3^3 + (4 \times 2.3) = 21.367$	Too small
2.4	$2.4^3 + (4 \times 2.4) = 23.424$	Too small
2.45	$2.45^3 + (4 \times 2.45) = 24.506...$	Too big

So the solution is between $x = 2.4$ and $x = 2.45$,
so to 1 d.p. the solution is $x = 2.4$
[4 marks available — 1 mark for any trial between 2 and 3, 1 mark for any trial between 2.4 and 2.5 inclusive, 1 mark for a different trial between 2.43 and 2.45 inclusive, 1 mark for the correct final answer]

2

x	$x^3 - 2x$	
1	$1^3 - (2 \times 1) = 1 - 2 = -1$	Too small
2	$2^3 - (2 \times 2) = 8 - 4 = 4$	Too big
1.5	$1.5^3 - (2 \times 1.5) = 0.375$	Too big
1.3	$1.3^3 - (2 \times 1.3) = -0.403$	Too small
1.4	$1.4^3 - (2 \times 1.4) = -0.056$	Too small
1.45	$1.45^3 - (2 \times 1.45) = 0.148...$	Too big

The solution is between $x = 1.4$ and $x = 1.45$,
so to 1 d.p. the solution is $x = 1.4$
[4 marks available — 1 mark for any trial between 1 and 2, 1 mark for any trial between 1.4 and 1.5 inclusive, 1 mark for a different trial between 1.42 and 1.45 inclusive, 1 mark for the correct final answer]

Page 39: Inequalities

1 $x \geq -2$ *[1 mark]*
It's ≥ because the circle above the number line is coloured in, so −2 is included.

2 −3, −2, −1, 0, 1
[2 marks available — 2 marks for all 5 numbers correct, otherwise 1 mark for the correct answer with one number missing or one number incorrect]

3 a) $2a - 7 \leq 11$
$2a \leq 11 + 7$
$2a \leq 18$ *[1 mark]*
$a \leq 18 \div 2$
$a \leq 9$ *[1 mark]*
[2 marks available in total — as above]

b)
[2 marks available — 1 mark for correct position of circle and direction of arrow, 1 mark for the circle filled in]

4 a) $2p > 4$
$p > 4 \div 2$
$p > 2$ *[1 mark]*

b) $4q - 5 < 23$
$4q < 23 + 5$
$4q < 28$ *[1 mark]*
$q < 28 \div 4$
$q < 7$ *[1 mark]*
[2 marks available in total — as above]

c) $4r - 2 \geq 2r + 5$
$4r - 2r \geq 5 + 2$
$2r \geq 7$ *[1 mark]*
$r \geq 7 \div 2$
$r \geq 3.5$ *[1 mark]*
[2 marks available in total — as above]

Section Three — Graphs

Pages 40-41: Coordinates and Midpoints

1 a) $(2, 1)$ *[1 mark]*

b) $(3, -2)$ *[1 mark]*

c)
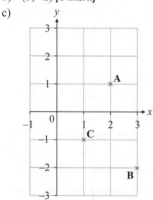
[1 mark]

2 a) $(1, 3)$ *[1 mark]*

b) $(1, 0)$ *[2 marks available — 2 marks for the correct answer, otherwise 1 mark for correctly drawing point S on graph]*

c) $(0, 4)$ *[2 marks available — 2 marks for the correct answer, otherwise 1 mark for correctly drawing point T on graph]*

3 a) $\left(\dfrac{1+3}{2}, \dfrac{3+(-1)}{2}\right) = (2, 1)$
[2 marks available — 1 mark for correct method and 1 mark for correct final answer]
A correct method here is to find the averages of the x- and y-coordinates. Alternatively, you could identify the midpoint of AB on the graph to get your answer — but the first way is much safer.

b) $(2, -1)$ is not on the line **BC** OR the midpoint of **BC** is actually $(2, -2)$ *[1 mark]*

4 a)
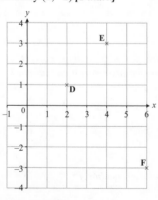
[1 mark]

b) $\left(\dfrac{2+4}{2}, \dfrac{1+3}{2}\right) = (3, 2)$
[2 marks available — 1 mark for correct method and 1 mark for correct final answer]

c) $\left(\dfrac{2+6}{2}, \dfrac{1+(-3)}{2}\right) = (4, -1)$
[2 marks available — 1 mark for correct method and 1 mark for correct final answer]

Pages 42-43: Straight-Line Graphs

1 a)

x	-2	-1	0	1	2
y	-8	-5	-2	1	4

[2 marks available — 2 marks for all values correct, otherwise 1 mark for 2 correct values]

b)
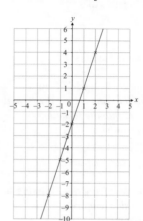
[2 marks available — 2 marks for all points plotted correctly and a straight line drawn from (–2, –8) to (2, 4), otherwise 1 mark for a correct straight line that passes through at least 3 correct points, or a straight line with the correct gradient, or a straight line with a positive gradient passing through (0, –2)]

c)

[3 marks available — 3 marks for a correct line drawn from (–2, 6) to (2, –2), otherwise 2 marks for a line that passes through (0, 2) and has a gradient of –2, or 1 mark for a line passing through (0, 2), or a line with a gradient of –2]

2 a)

x	-2	-1	0	1	2
y	14	11	8	5	2

[2 marks available — 2 marks for all values correct, otherwise 1 mark for 2 correct values]

b)

[2 marks available — 2 marks for all points plotted correctly and a straight line drawn from (–2, 14) to (2, 2), otherwise 1 mark for a correct straight line that passes through at least 3 correct points, or a straight line with the correct gradient, or a straight line with a negative gradient passing through (0, 8)]

Answers

3 a)

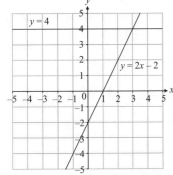

[3 marks available — 3 marks for a correct line drawn from (–1, –4) to (3, 4), otherwise 2 marks for a line that passes through (0, –2) and has a gradient of 2, or 1 mark for a line that passes through (0, –2), or a line with a gradient of 2]

b) $x = 3$, $y = 4$

[3 marks available — 1 mark for a correct line (as on graph above), 1 mark for a correct value of x, 1 mark for a correct value of y]

4 gradient = 3 *[1 mark]*

5 a) $y = 4x - 1$ *[1 mark]*

b) E.g. No, they are not parallel because they do not have the same gradient. *[1 mark]*

Pages 44-45: Travel Graphs

1 a) $\frac{15 - 0}{1 - 0} = \frac{15}{1} = 15$ km/h

[2 marks available — 1 mark for a correct method, 1 mark for correct final answer]

b) The speed at which Selby was travelling. *[1 mark]*

c) 3 hours *[1 mark]*

As he was at point A at 0 hours, all you have to do is read off the x-value at point C to see how long Selby's journey was.

d) 2.5 hours *[1 mark]*

e)

[2 marks available — 1 mark for a flat line from point E for 30 minutes, and 1 mark for a straight line from the end of the flat line to (7, 0)]

f) $7 - 0.5 - 2.5 - 0.5 = 3.5$ hours *[1 mark]*

Selby isn't cycling whenever the graph shows a horizontal line. So, subtract these times from the total amount of time he is out.

2 a) 1.25 hours *[1 mark]*

b)

[2 marks available — 1 mark for a horizontal line between (2.75, 90) and (3.5, 90), and 1 mark for line from (3.5, 90) to (5.5, 0) or a line parallel to this starting at the wrong point]

c) 5 hours 30 minutes *[1 mark]*

d) 1 45 pm and 2 45 pm *[1 mark]*

The steeper the gradient, the faster the person is travelling. The gradient is steepest between 1 45 pm and 2 45 pm.

3 a)

[3 marks available — 1 mark for line from (1, 0) to (3, 7), 1 mark for horizontal line for 3 hours and 45 minutes from (3, 7), 1 mark for line from (6.75, 7) to (7, 0)]

b) speed = $\frac{\text{distance}}{\text{time}}$, so $\frac{7}{0.25} = 28$ mph

[2 marks available — 1 mark for a correct method, 1 mark for correct final answer]

Page 46: Conversion Graphs

1 a) 36 litres (allow 35 – 37 litres) *[1 mark]*

b) 4.5 gallons (allow 4.3 – 4.5 gallons) *[1 mark]*

c) 40 litres = 8.8 gallons (allow 8.6 – 9.0 gallons)
$40 \times 2 = 80$, so 8.8 gallons $\times 2 = 17.6$ gallons
(allow 17.2 – 18.0 gallons)

[3 marks available — 1 mark for correct conversion factor, 1 mark for correct application of the conversion factor and 1 mark for answer within the range 17.2 – 18.0]

2 a)

[2 marks available — 2 marks for all 3 points plotted correctly and a straight line drawn through the points, otherwise 1 mark for at least 1 point plotted correctly and a straight line drawn through points]

b) 78 °F *[1 mark for an answer between 78 °F and 79 °F]*

c) 36 °C *[1 mark for an answer between 35 °C and 36 °C]*

Page 47: Real-Life Graphs

1 a)

Number of items	0	5	10	20
Cost (£)	5	**10**	**15**	25

[2 marks available — 1 mark for each correct value]

b)

[2 marks available — 1 mark for all points plotted correctly, 1 mark for a straight line drawn through points]

c) 25 items *[1 mark]*

2 a) (i) £18 *[1 mark]*
   (ii) 40 ÷ 100 *[1 mark]*
       = 0.4, so it costs 40p per unit *[1 mark]*
   [2 marks available in total — as above]

b) Mr Barker should use Plan A because it is cheaper. Using 85 units with Plan A would cost £26.50. 85 units with Plan B would cost £34.
   [2 marks available — 1 mark for correctly stating which plan, 1 mark for giving a reason]

Page 48: Quadratic Graphs

1 a)

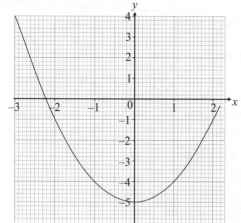

[2 marks available — 1 mark if all points are plotted correctly, 1 mark for a smooth curve joining the correctly plotted points]

b) –2.2 (allow –2.3 to –2.1) *[1 mark]*

2 a)

x	–4	–3	–2	–1	0	1	2
y	8	3	0	–1	0	3	8

[1 mark]

b)

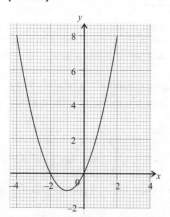

[2 marks available — 1 mark if all points are plotted correctly, 1 mark for a smooth curve joining the correctly plotted points]

c) 1.6 metres (allow 1.5 – 1.8 metres)
   [2 marks available — 1 mark for indicating 6 on the y-axis, 1 mark for the correct final answer]
   If the width of the pool is x and the length is (x + 2), then the area is x(x + 2), and you can use the graph to find when x(x + 2) = 6.

Section Four — Shapes and Area

Pages 49-50: Symmetry

1 a)

[1 mark]

b)

 or *[1 mark]*

2 a)

[2 marks available — 1 mark for each correct line of symmetry]

b) 2 *[1 mark]*

3 a) A and B
   [2 marks available — 1 mark for each correct letter]

b) E *[1 mark]*

c)

 [1 mark]

4 E.g.

[2 marks available — 2 marks for this or any other correct plane of symmetry, otherwise 1 mark if just a line of symmetry on one face is drawn]

Page 51: Properties of 2D Shapes

1 a) Equilateral triangle *[1 mark]*
   You need to say "equilateral triangle" to get the mark, not just "triangle".

b) C *[1 mark]*

2 E.g.

[2 marks available — 1 mark for 2 pairs of equal sides, 1 mark for 2 pairs of equal angles]
Read the information carefully — there's only one type of shape this could be.

3 E.g.

[1 mark]

There isn't just one right answer here — as long as your shape has four sides, with two of them parallel, you'll get the mark.

4 a) No lines of symmetry *[1 mark]*
   b) Order 2 *[1 mark]*

Page 52: Congruence and Similarity

1

a) *[1 mark for shapes correctly labelled 'C' — as above]*
b) *[1 mark for shapes correctly labelled 'S' — as above]*

2 a) Triangle *AEX [1 mark]*
   b) Triangle *AYX [1 mark]*

3 A and F *[1 mark]*
   C and D *[1 mark]*
   [2 marks available in total — as above]

Page 53: 3D Shapes

1 A = Sphere *[1 mark]*
   B = Cone *[1 mark]*
   [2 marks available in total — as above]

2 a) 6 *[1 mark]*
   b) 12 *[1 mark]*
   c) 8 *[1 mark]*

3 a) Pyramid or square-based pyramid *[1 mark]*
   b) 6 *[1 mark]*
   c) B *[1 mark]*
   d) D *[1 mark]*

Page 54: Projections

1

[3 marks available — 1 mark for a width of 6 squares, 1 mark for a height of 9 squares, 1 mark for a correct dotted or solid line marking the edge of the roof]

2

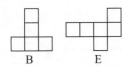

Front elevation   Plan view

[4 marks available in total — 2 marks for a correct front elevation diagram, otherwise 1 mark for a correct shape with one error in dimensions, and 2 marks for a correct plan view diagram in any orientation, otherwise 1 mark for a T-shaped diagram with the wrong dimensions]

3

A   D   B   E

[4 marks available in total — 1 mark for each correct letter]

Pages 55-56: Perimeters and Areas

1 a) 18 cm *[1 mark]*
   b) 14 cm² *[1 mark]*

2 a) $6.4 \times 10 = 64$ cm²
      [2 marks available — 1 mark for correct calculation, 1 mark for correct answer]
   b) $\sqrt{64} = 8$ cm
      [2 marks available — 1 mark for correct calculation, 1 mark for correct answer]

3 Area of rectangle = $6 \times 8 = 48$ cm² *[1 mark]*
   Base of triangle = 8 cm − 5 cm = 3 cm *[1 mark]*
   Area of triangle = $\frac{1}{2} \times 3 \times 4 = 6$ cm² *[1 mark]*
   Area of shaded area = 48 − 6 *[1 mark]* = 42 cm² *[1 mark]*
   [5 marks available in total — as above]

4 Area of field = ½ × (105 + 80) × 60 = 5550 m² *[1 mark]*
   Price of weedkiller per m² = 0.27 ÷ 10 = £0.027 *[1 mark]*
   Cost = area × price per square metre = 5550 × 0.027 *[1 mark]*
   = £149.85 *[1 mark]*
   [4 marks available in total — as above]

5 a) Area of patio = $5 \times 5 = 25$ m² *[1 mark]*
      Area of lawn and patio = $27 \times 10 = 270$ m² *[1 mark]*
      Area of lawn = 270 − 25 = 245 m² *[1 mark]*
      245 ÷ 10 = 24.5, so 25 boxes needed. *[1 mark]*
      Cost = no. of boxes × price per box = 25 × 7 *[1 mark]*
      = £175.00 *[1 mark]*
      [6 marks available in total — as above]
   b) Perimeter of lawn = 10 + 22 + 5 + 5 + 5 + 27 = 74 m *[1 mark]*
      No. of strips = perimeter ÷ length of strip = 74 ÷ 2 *[1 mark]*
      = 37 strips *[1 mark]*
      [3 marks available in total — as above]

Pages 57-58: Circles

1 a) Diameter *[1 mark]*
   b) Radius *[1 mark]*
   c) Chord *[1 mark]*
   d)

[1 mark for line drawn at right angles to the end of the diameter at A]

2 Circumference = $3.14 \times (2 \times 0.25)$ *[1 mark]* = 1.57 m *[1 mark]*
   [2 marks available in total — as above]

3 a) 19.5×13 *[1 mark]* = 253.5 cm² *[1 mark]*
      [2 marks available in total — as above]
   b) Radius of biscuit = 13 ÷ 4 = 3.25 cm *[1 mark]*
      Area of biscuit = $\pi r^2 = \pi \times 3.25^2$ *[1 mark]*
      = 33.2 cm² (to 1 d.p.) *[1 mark]*
      [3 marks available in total — as above]

4 Area of outside circle = $\pi \times 5^2 = 78.53...$ cm² *[1 mark]*
   Area of inside circle = $\pi \times 3^2 = 28.27...$ cm² *[1 mark]*
   Area of letter "O" = 78.53... − 28.27... *[1 mark]*
   = 50.3 cm² (to 3 s.f) *[1 mark]*
   [4 marks available in total — as above]

5 Area of square = $8 \times 8 = 64$ m² *[1 mark]*
   Area of circle = $\pi \times 4^2$ *[1 mark]* = 50.26... m² *[1 mark]*
   Area of grass = 64 − 50.26... = 13.73... m² *[1 mark]*
   No. of packets = 13.73... ÷ 0.5 = 27.469... *[1 mark]*
   So he will need 28 packets. *[1 mark]*
   [6 marks available in total — as above]

6   Area of cookie = π × 5² *[1 mark]* = 78.53... cm² *[1 mark]*
    78.53... ÷ 3 *[1 mark]* = 26.17... *[1 mark]*
    So the maximum number of buttons is 26. *[1 mark]*
    [5 marks available in total — as above]

Pages 59-60: Volume

1   Area of cross-section is 7 squares and the length is 3 cubes,
    so volume = 7 × 3 = 21 cm³
    [2 marks available — 1 mark for correct method,
    1 mark for correct answer]

2   Volume = 6 × 10 × 14 = 840 cm³
    [2 marks available — 1 mark for correct calculation,
    1 mark for correct answer]

3   Area of cross-section = π × 1² = 3.141... m² *[1 mark]*
    Volume of paddling pool = height × area of cross-section
    = 0.4 × 3.141... *[1 mark]*
    = 1.26 m³ (to 2 d.p.) *[1 mark]*
    [3 marks available in total — as above]

4   Area of cross-section = $\frac{1}{2}$ × 6 × 4 = 12 cm² *[1 mark]*
    Volume of prism = 12 × 4 *[1 mark]* = 48 cm³ *[1 mark]*
    [3 marks available in total — as above]

5   a)   Volume = 90 × 40 × 30 *[1 mark]* = 108 000 cm³ *[1 mark]*
         [2 marks available in total — as above]

    b)   Number of fish = 108 000 ÷ 6000 = 18
         So the greatest number of fish the tank can hold is 18.
         [2 marks available — 1 mark for correct calculation,
         1 mark for correct answer]

6   40 ÷ 8 = 5, so exactly 5 boxes fit into the width of each case.
    16 ÷ 8 = 2, so exactly 2 boxes fit into the height of each case.
    50 ÷ 8 = 6.25, so you can only fit 6 boxes along the length of the
    case, with a small gap at the end.
    So each case can take a maximum of 5 × 2 × 6 = 60 boxes of fudge.
    [3 marks available — 1 mark for a correct method, 1 mark for at
    least one division correct, and 1 mark for the correct final answer]
    You need to think practically here — if you divided the volume of the
    case by the volume of one box, you'd get 62.5. But you can't put bits of
    boxes in to fill gaps. So you need to stop and think about what the best
    way of packing whole boxes into the case is.

Pages 61-62: Nets and Surface Area

1   E.g.

    [2 marks available — 1 mark for each correctly drawn face]

2   A *[1 mark]*

3   a)   E.g.

    1 cm   1 cm
    ↔   ↔
                        ↕ 1 cm

                              5 cm
    4 cm   4 cm
                        ↕ 1 cm

    [3 marks available in total — 3 marks for a correct and
    accurately drawn diagram, otherwise 1 mark for a net of any
    cuboid, or 2 marks for a net with five faces correct]
    There are several ways to make a cuboid net, so the faces in your
    net could be in different places relative to each other.

b) Area of front = 4 × 1 = 4 cm²
    Area of side = 5 × 1 = 5 cm²
    Area of top = 4 × 5 = 20 cm²
    Total surface area = 2 × (4 + 5 + 20) = 58 cm²
    [3 marks available — 1 mark for finding the area of each face,
    1 mark for adding the areas, 1 mark for the correct final answer]

4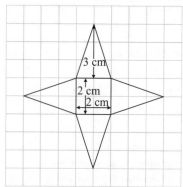

    3 cm
    2 cm
    2 cm

    [3 marks available in total — 3 marks for a correct and accurately
    drawn diagram, otherwise 1 mark for a square and 4 triangles with
    the wrong measurements, or 2 marks for a correctly-sized square
    and 4 isosceles triangles with the wrong measurements]
    There are other ways of drawing this net, but this is really the only
    sensible way of doing it.

5   Surface area = (2 × 2m × 1m) + (2 × 2m × 0.03 m) +
    (2 × 1 m × 0.03 m) = 4.18 m²
    Dan needs enough varnish to cover 4.18 m² × 2 = 8.36 m².
    8.36 m² ÷ 2.45 m² = 3.4122... tins. So Dan should buy 4 tins.
    [4 marks available — 1 mark for a correct method for finding the
    surface area, 1 mark for the correct surface area, 1 mark for a
    correct method for calculating the number of tins, and 1 mark for
    the correct final answer]
    Don't forget you need to round up here — not down. 3 tins wouldn't be
    enough, since you've worked out that Dan needs 3.4122... tins.

6   Area of triangle = ½ × 6.0 × 5.2 = 15.6 cm²
    Area of whole octahedron = 8 × 15.6 = 124.8 cm²
    [3 marks available — 1 mark for a correct method for finding the
    area of the triangle, 1 mark for the correct triangle area, 1 mark
    for the correct final answer]

Section Five — Angles and Geometry

Pages 63-64: Measuring and Drawing Lines and Angles

1   a)   11 cm *[1 mark, allow ± 1 mm]*

    b)
         Measure to check your cross is 5.5 cm from either end.

2   a)

         [1 mark for a cross 2.5 cm from point A as shown, ± 1 mm]

    b)   9 cm *[1 mark, allow ± 1 mm]*

    c)   34° *[1 mark for any answer between 33° and 35°]*

    d)   Acute angle *[1 mark]* *(writing 'acute' is OK too)*

3   Reflex angle *[1 mark]*

4   a)
         A   D
         R
                  or
         R
         B   C
                              x

         [1 mark for either angle marked]

    b)   4.9 cm *[1 mark, allow ± 1 mm]*

Answers

c) Obtuse angle *[1 mark]*

d) 115° *[1 mark for any answer between 114° and 116°]*

5

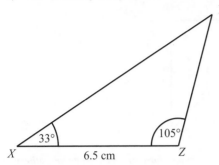

(This diagram isn't actual size — but your measurements should match those given above.)

[3 marks available in total — 1 mark for a 6.5 cm line drawn (± 1 mm), 1 mark for correct angles drawn at the ends of this line (± 1°), 1 mark for a fully correct diagram]

Measure to check the length of your lines and the size of your angles — make sure you've labelled your diagram too.

Pages 65-66: Five Angle Rules

1 Angles on a straight line add up to 180°, so $x + 30° + 50° = 180°$. *[1 mark]*
$x = 180° - 50° - 30° = 100°$. *[1 mark]*
[2 marks available in total — as above]

2 $110° + 170° + 50° + 40° = 370°$. *[1 mark]*
Angles round a point add up to 360°, not 370°, so these angles do not fit round a point as they are shown on the diagram. *[1 mark]*
[2 marks available in total — as above]

3 a) $x + 60° + 74° = 180°$
(*angles in a triangle add up to 180°*)
So $x = 180° - 74° - 60° = 46°$
[2 marks available — 1 mark for a correct method, 1 mark for the correct answer]

   b) $x + y = 180°$ (*angles on a straight line add up to 180°*)
$46° + y = 180°$, so $y = 180° - 46° = 134°$
[2 marks available — 1 mark for a correct method, 1 mark for the correct answer]

4 $70° + 90° + 97° = 257°$
Angle $ADC = 360° - 257° = 103°$
(*angles in a quadrilateral add up to 360°*)
[2 marks available — 1 mark for a correct method, 1 mark for the correct answer]

5 $180° - 48° = 132° =$ Angles $ACB + BAC$ *[1 mark]*
(*angles in a triangle add up to 180°*)
Angle $ACB = 132° ÷ 2 = 66°$ *[1 mark]* (*ABC is isosceles*)
Angle $BCD = 180° - 66° = 114°$ *[1 mark]*
(*angles on a straight line add up to 180°*)
[3 marks available in total — as above]

6 Angle $CBE = 180° - 115° = 65°$ *[1 mark]*
Angle $BED = 180° - 103° = 77°$ *[1 mark]*
because angles on a straight line add up to 180°. *[1 mark]*
Angles in a quadrilateral add up to 360° *[1 mark]* so:
$x + 90° + 77° + 65° = 360°$ (*CDE is a right angle*)
$x + 232° = 360°$
$x = 360° - 232° = 128°$ *[1 mark]*
[5 marks available in total — as above]
Make sure you've answered this one in clear sentences, since you're marked on the quality of your written communication.

7 Angles in a triangle add up to 180°. $180° - 96° = 84°$, *[1 mark]*
so angle $VYX = 84° ÷ 2 = 42°$, because isosceles triangles have 2 equal angles. *[1 mark]* Angles on a straight line add up to 180°, so angle $UYZ = 180° - 90° - 42°$ *[1 mark]* $= 48°$ *[1 mark]*
[4 marks available in total — as above]

Page 67: Parallel Lines

1 a)

[1 mark]

   b) Line SR *[1 mark]*

2 $a = 75°$ *[1 mark]* because vertically opposite angles are equal. *[1 mark]*
[2 marks available in total — as above]

3 Angle $JBC = 35°$ (*vertically opposite angles*)
Angle $BCK = 150°$ (*corresponding angles*)
Angle $BCJ = 180° - 150° = 30°$ *[1 mark]*
(*angles on a straight line add up to 180°*)
$x° = 180° - (35° + 30°)$ *[1 mark]* $= 115°$ *[1 mark]*
(*angles in a triangle add up to 180°*)
[3 marks available in total — as above]

4 Angle $BDE = 117°$ (*corresponding angles*)
Angle $CED = 30°$ (*vertically opposite angles*)
Angle $CDE =$ Angle $CED = 30°$ *[1 mark]* (*isosceles triangle*)
$x =$ Angle $BDE -$ Angle CDE *[1 mark]*
$= 117° - 30° = 87°$ *[1 mark]*
[3 marks available in total — as above]
There are other ways to find x. For instance, angle CBD = 180° − 117° = 63° (angles on a straight line), angle BCD = CDE (alternate angles) = 30° (see above), so x = 180° − 63° − 30° = 87° (angles in a triangle).

Page 68: Polygons and Angles

1 A regular octagon *[1 mark]*

2 Sum of interior angles of a pentagon $= (5 - 3) × 180°$ *[1 mark]*
$= 540°$ *[1 mark]*
$p = 540° - 90° - 94° - 102° - 119°$ *[1 mark]* $= 135°$ *[1 mark]*
[4 marks available in total — as above]

3 a) Exterior angle $= 360° ÷ 6 = 60°$ *[1 mark]*
Interior angle $= 180° - 60° = 120°$ *[1 mark]*
[2 marks available in total — as above]

   b) Each angle in an equilateral triangle is 60°.
The interior angle of a regular hexagon is 120°.
Angles round a point add up to 360°. *[1 mark]*
$60° + 60° + 120° + 120° = 360°$, *[1 mark]*
so 2 regular hexagons and 2 equilateral triangles can meet at a point. *[1 mark]*
[3 marks available in total — as above]

Pages 69-71: Transformations

1

[1 mark]

2

[2 marks available — 2 marks for correct reflection, otherwise 1 mark for triangle reflected but in wrong position]

3 a)

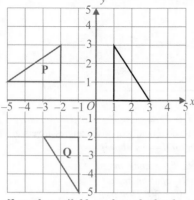

[3 marks available — 3 marks for the correct rotation, otherwise 2 marks for a correct rotation but from the wrong centre, or 1 mark for 2 points correctly rotated]

b) Rotation *[1 mark]* 90° anticlockwise *[1 mark]* about the origin *[1 mark]*
[3 marks available in total — as above]

4 a) Translation *[1 mark]* by the vector $\begin{pmatrix} 1 \\ -7 \end{pmatrix}$ *[1 mark]*.

[2 marks available in total — as above, or with the vector described in words]

b)

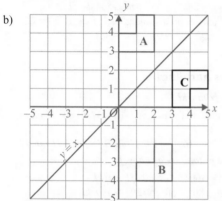

[2 marks available — 2 marks for the correct reflection, otherwise 1 mark for the correctly reflected shape in the wrong position]

c) Rotation *[1 mark]* of 180° *[1 mark]* about the point (3, –1) *[1 mark]*
[3 marks available in total — as above]

5 a)

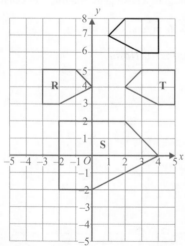

[1 mark]

b) Reflection *[1 mark]* in the line $x = 1$ *[1 mark]*.
[2 marks available in total — as above]

c) Enlargement *[1 mark]* of scale factor 2 *[1 mark]*, centre (–4, 8) *[1 mark]*.
[3 marks available in total — as above]

6

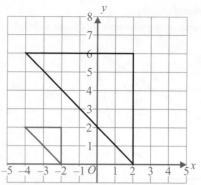

[3 marks available — 3 marks for correct enlargement, otherwise 2 marks for a correct triangle but in the wrong position or for an enlargement from the correct centre but of the wrong scale factor, or 1 mark for 2 lines enlarged by the correct scale factor anywhere on the grid]

7 Reflection in the y-axis / in the line $x = 0$.

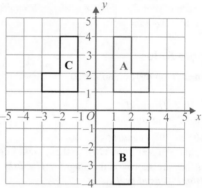

[4 marks available — 1 mark for correct position of B, 1 mark for correct position of C, 1 mark for reflection, 1 mark for mirror line]

Page 72: Similar Shape Problems

1 a) True *[1 mark]*
   b) True *[1 mark]*
   c) False *[1 mark]*

2 $x = 18 \times 2.5 = 45$ *[1 mark]*
  $y = 24 \times 2.5 = 60$ *[1 mark]*
  [2 marks available in total — as above]

3

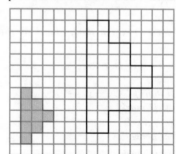

[2 marks available — 2 marks for the correct shape anywhere on the grid, pointing in any direction, otherwise 1 mark for a correct enlargement by a scale factor that's greater than 2, or 1 mark for 2 sides correct but others incorrect]

Answers

Page 73: Triangle Construction

For these questions measure your construction to check it's accurately drawn.

1

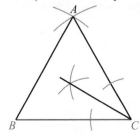

a) *[1 mark for correct arcs at point A with straight lines joining B and C to the point where they cross]*

b) *[2 marks available — 1 mark for compass arcs, 1 mark for bisector accurately drawn]*

2

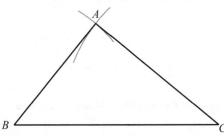

[3 marks available — 1 mark for BC within 1 mm of 5.6 cm, 1 mark for AB within 1 mm of 3.5 cm if correct construction arc is shown, 1 mark for AC within 1 mm of 4.3 cm if correct construction arc is shown]

Pages 74-75: Loci and Constructions

1

[3 marks available — 1 mark for marks using the radius spaced around the circle, 2 marks for correct regular hexagon drawn within the circle, otherwise 1 mark for any hexagon drawn within the circle]

You construct a regular hexagon by setting your compass to the radius of the circle, then putting the pointy bit onto the edge of the circle. You draw an arc crossing the circle, then you move your compass so the pointy bit is on that arc, and draw another arc. Keep going until you've got six arcs, join them all together with straight lines, and you're done.

2

a) *[2 marks available — 1 mark for construction marks, 1 mark for point S drawn 4.2 cm from P and 6.7 cm from R]*

Be as accurate as you can with the measurements, but you'll still get the marks if you are within 1 mm of the above lengths.

b) *[2 marks available — 1 mark for construction arcs, 1 mark for the perpendicular]*

3

Scale: 1 cm represents 5 m

(diagram not actual size)

[2 marks available — 2 marks for arcs with a radius of 2 cm centred at A and B, lines 2 cm either side of AB and correct area shaded, otherwise 1 mark for arcs with a radius of 2 cm centred at A and B or for lines 2 cm either side of AB]

You'll still get the marks if you are within 1 mm of the correct measurements.

4

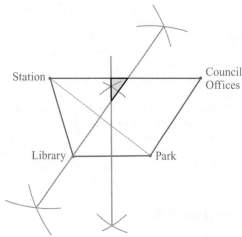

[5 marks available — 1 mark for each pair of correct arcs (centred at Library and Park and at Station and Park), 1 mark for each correct perpendicular bisector (of line between Library and Park and line between Station and Park), 1 mark for correct shaded area]

5

[4 marks available — 1 mark for arcs with radius of 1 cm centred at B and C, 1 mark for a line 1 cm from BC , 1 mark for an arc with radius of 2 cm centred at F, 1 mark for correct crosses at the intersections]

Page 76: Pythagoras' Theorem

1 $2.1^2 + x^2 = 3.5^2$ *[1 mark]*

$x^2 = 3.5^2 - 2.1^2$

$x^2 = 12.25 - 4.41 = 7.84$

$x = \sqrt{7.84}$ *[1 mark]*

$x = 2.8$

2.8 m *[1 mark]*

[3 marks available in total — as above]

2

The garden is a rectangle, so the side AD is also 30 m.
The distance round the edge from A to C is 30 m + 40 m = 70 m.
[1 mark]
Let the distance across the diagonal from point A to point C be x m.
By Pythagoras' theorem $30^2 + 40^2 = x^2$ *[1 mark]*
$x = \sqrt{900 + 1600} = \sqrt{2500} = 50$ m *[1 mark]*
The price for laying the pipe across the diagonal is £8.35 per metre plus
the cost of digging the trench and replacing the grass:
$£202.50 + (50 \times £8.35) = £620.00$ *[1 mark]*
The price for laying the pipe around the edge is £8.35 per metre:
$70 \times £8.35 = £584.50$ *[1 mark]*
It is cheaper to lay the pipe round the edge — it will cost £620.00 to lay
the pipe across the diagonal and only £584.50 to lay it around the edge.
***[1 mark for concluding that it's cheaper to lay the pipe round the
edge, if the cost of each has been worked out above]***
[6 marks available in total — as above]
*Alternatively, instead of working out the cost of each option, you could work
out the cost of the extra 20 m of pipe needed to go around the edge of the
field, and show that this is less than the cost of digging a trench.*

Section Six — Measures

Pages 77-78: Units and Conversions

1 a)

	Imperial	**Metric**
Length of a car	feet	metres
Weight of a rabbit	pounds	kilograms
Volume of a milk jug	pints	litres

[3 marks available — 1 mark for each correct answer]
b) 8.87 m *[1 mark]*
c) 1300 g *[1 mark]*

2 2.5 litres × 1000 = 2500 ml
2500 ÷ 250 = 10 cups
*[3 marks available — 1 mark for converting litres to ml, 1 mark
for dividing by 250, and 1 mark for final answer]*
*A correct method here could also be to convert 250 ml into litres
(0.25 litres) and then divide 2.5 by 0.25.*

3 2500 g ÷ 1000 = 2.5 kg *[1 mark]*
Convert kg into lb: 2.5 × 2.2 = 5.5 lb *[1 mark]*
5.5 ÷ 1.5 = 3.6666... *[1 mark]*
Maximum number of books = 3 *[1 mark]*
[4 marks available in total — as above]

4 a) 40 km into miles = $\frac{5 \times 40}{8}$ *[1 mark]*
= 25 miles *[1 mark]*
[2 marks available in total — as above]

b) 60 km/h into mph = $\frac{5 \times 60}{8}$ = 37.5 mph *[1 mark]*
Since 37.5 mph is less than 40 mph, the camel would
outrun a giraffe. *[1 mark]*
[2 marks available in total — as above]

5 14 pints into litres: 14 ÷ 1.75 = 8 litres *[1 mark]*
= 8000 ml *[1 mark]*
$(3 \times 720$ ml$) + (5 \times 520$ ml$) = 4760$ ml *[1 mark]*
8000 ml − 4760 ml = 3240 ml left *[1 mark]*
3240 ÷ 540 = 6 times *[1 mark]*
[5 marks available in total — as above]

6 39 200 ÷ 100 = 392
392 ÷ 100 = 3.92 m²
*[2 marks available — 1 mark for correct method and 1 mark
for correct final answer]*
*When the unit is squared, you have to use the conversion factor twice (so
you use 100, and then 100 again). You could also divide 39 200 by
10 000 instead.*

Page 79: Reading Scales

1 a) 5 °C *[1 mark]*
b) 78 mph *[1 mark]*
c) 15 oz *[1 mark]*
2 a) 55 ml *[1 mark]*
b) 55 − 15
= 40 ml *[1 mark]*
[2 marks available in total — as above]
3 a) 40.6 m *[1 mark]*
b)

[1 mark]

Page 80: Rounding and Estimating Measurements

1 Average height of a man ≈ 180 cm (allow 150 − 210 cm,
or 5 ft − 6 ft 6 inches) *[1 mark]*
height of penguin ≈ 180 ÷ 3 *[1 mark]*
= 60 cm (accept 50 − 67 cm) *[1 mark]*
[3 marks available in total — as above]

2 a) −1.6 °C *[1 mark]*
b)

[1 mark]
c) 2.5 °C *[1 mark]*

3 Minimum weight = 56.5 kg *[1 mark]*
Maximum weight = 57.5 kg *[1 mark]*
[2 marks available in total — as above]

Page 81: Reading Timetables

1 a) 11:15 am *[1 mark]*
b) 10:30 am + 8 hrs = 6:30 pm *[1 mark]*
2 a) 11 15 − 25 min *[1 mark]*
= 10 50 *[1 mark]*
[2 marks available in total — as above]
b) 11 35 → 13 22 = 1 h 47 min *[1 mark]*
= 107 minutes *[1 mark]*
[2 marks available in total — as above]
3 a) 17 04 *[1 mark]*
b) 6 minutes *[1 mark]*
c) 16 40 → 18 15 *[1 mark]*
= 1 h 35 mins *[1 mark]*
[2 marks available in total — as above]

Page 82: Compass Directions and Bearings

1 a) F2 *[1 mark]*
b) Devil's Glen *[1 mark]*
c) Thunder Ride *[1 mark]*

d) South West *[1 mark]*

2 a) 035° (accept 034° – 036°) *[1 mark]*

b)

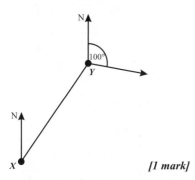

[1 mark]

Page 83: Maps and Scale Drawings

1 a) Drawing of dining table is 4 cm long.
So 4 cm is equivalent to 2 m.
2 ÷ 4 = 0.5
Therefore scale is 1 cm to 0.5 m *[1 mark]*

b) On drawing, dining table is 3 cm from shelves.
So real distance = 3 × 0.5 = 1.5 m *[1 mark]*

c) Length of drawing of room = 10 cm
So length of real room = 10 × 0.5 = 5 m *[1 mark]*
Width of drawing of room = 6 cm
So width of real room = 6 × 0.5 = 3 m *[1 mark]*
Area of room = 5 m × 3 m = 15 m² *[1 mark]*
[3 marks available in total — as above]

2 a) 4 × 200 000 = 800 000 cm = 8 km (allow 7.6 – 8.4 km) *[1 mark]*

b) 7 km = 700 000 cm
700 000 ÷ 200 000 = 3.5 cm *[1 mark]*

Page 84: Speed and Density

1 speed = $\frac{\text{distance}}{\text{time}}$, so speed × time = distance *[1 mark]*
= 56 × 1.25 = 70 km *[1 mark]*
[2 marks available in total — as above]

2 Friday: speed = 5 ÷ 0.75 = 6.66... mph
Saturday: speed = 26 ÷ 3.25 = 8 mph
Sunday: speed = 33 ÷ 3.75 = 8.8 mph
so, Beatrix rode fastest on Sunday
*[4 marks available — 1 mark for attempting to divide a
distance by a time, 1 mark for getting one speed correct,
1 mark for getting the other two speeds correct,
1 mark for a correct final answer]*

3 Volume = 360 ÷ 1800 *[1 mark]*
= 0.2 m³ *[1 mark]*
[2 marks available in total — as above]

Section Seven — Statistics and Probability

Page 85: Collecting Data

1 E.g. No time frame is given. / The response boxes do not cover all
possible outcomes. / The response boxes overlap.
*[2 marks available — 1 mark for each of the above,
up to a maximum of 2]*

2 a) E.g. No time frame is specified, so the response boxes are vague
and could be interpreted differently by different people / the
response boxes do not cover all possible answers.
[1 mark]

b) E.g. The results of his survey are likely to be biased as he is only
asking boys who like football.
[1 mark]

Page 86: Mean, Median, Mode and Range

1 a) In ascending order: 3, 10, 12, 12, 13, 18, 25, 33, 37, 41
Median = (13 + 18) ÷ 2 = 15.5 minutes
*[2 marks available — 1 mark for ordering the
numbers in ascending or descending order and 1 mark for
correctly working out the median]*

b) Mean = (3 + 10 + 12 + 12 + 13 + 18 + 25 + 33 + 37 + 41) ÷ 10
= 204 ÷ 10 *[1 mark]* = 20.4 minutes
= 20 minutes (to the nearest minute) *[1 mark]*
[2 marks available in total — as above]

c) Range = 41 – 3 *[1 mark]* = 38 minutes *[1 mark]*
[2 marks available in total — as above]

2 a) £18 000 *[1 mark]*

b) £18 000 *[1 mark]*

c) Mean for Company A
= (18 000 + 18 000 + 18 000 + 25 200 + 38 500) ÷ 5
= 117 700 ÷ 5 *[1 mark]* = £23 540 *[1 mark]*, so Company A has a
lower mean annual salary than Company B. *[1 mark]*
[3 marks available in total — as above]

3 1, 4, 7
*[2 marks available — 2 marks for all three numbers correct,
otherwise 1 mark for 3 numbers that have a range of 6 and a mean
of 4 but aren't all different, or 3 different numbers that add up to
12 or that have a range of 6]*

Page 87: Tables

1 a) The Ivy *[1 mark]*

b) 2 *[1 mark]*

2 Cost in June = 2 × £300 + 3 × £290 = £1470
Cost in July = 2 × £330 + 3 × £275 = £1485
So it would be cheaper for the Whites to go for a week in June.
*[4 marks available — 1 mark for multiplying by 2 for the adult
price and by 3 for the child price, 1 mark for using the correct
adult and child prices from the table, 1 mark for the correct
total cost in June and the correct total cost in July,
1 mark for clearly stating that June is cheaper]*

Page 88: Pictograms

1 a) 40 *[1 mark]*

b)

[1 mark]

c) Blackberry Jam *[1 mark]*

2 a) 30 *[1 mark]*

b) 40 – 20 = 20 *[1 mark]*

c)

| Thursday | ◯ ◯ ◯ |
| Friday | ◯ ◯ ◁ |

*[2 marks available — 1 mark for three full circles drawn for
Thursday and 1 mark for two and a quarter circles drawn for
Friday]*

Page 89: Bar Charts

1 a) 25 *[1 mark]*

b) Tuesday *[1 mark]*

c)

[2 marks available — 1 mark for a light shaded bar drawn to 45 and 1 mark for a dark shaded bar drawn to 30]

d) No. of cups of tea sold = 50 + 40 + 25 + 70 + 45 = 230
No. of cups of coffee sold = 30 + 55 + 60 + 50 + 30 = 225
So, there were more cups of tea sold in total.
[2 marks available — 1 mark for finding both totals, 1 mark for the correct answer]

2

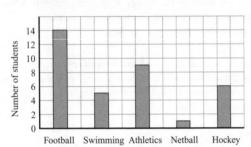

[3 marks available — 1 mark for a suitable scale, 1 mark for a fully labelled bar chart, 1 mark for all bar heights correct]

Page 90: Two-Way Tables

1

	Left-Handed	Right-Handed	Total
Male	9	51	60
Female	14	126	140
Total	23	177	200

[4 marks available — 1 mark for each correct value]

2 a) E.g.

	Girls	Boys	Total
Swimming			
Athletics			
Football			
Total			

[3 marks available — 3 marks for a correct table, otherwise 2 marks for a two-way table with one error or missing label, or 1 mark for a two-way table with two errors or missing labels]
The labels can be in a different order or the other way around.

b)

	Girls	Boys	Total
Swimming			
Athletics	32		
Football			
Total			

[1 mark]

Page 91: Time Series

1 a)

[2 marks available — 2 marks for all 7 points plotted correctly and straight lines drawn between them, otherwise 1 mark for at least 4 points plotted correctly with straight lines drawn between them]

b) Tuesday 6th August *[1 mark]*

c) Sunday 11th August and Monday 12th August as the number of sales was much lower on those days.
[2 marks available — 1 mark for both dates correct, 1 mark for a correct explanation]

d) The number of sales will probably be the same as the last few days as the weather is similar.
[2 marks available — 1 mark for plotting a point between 34 and 38, 1 mark for a correct explanation for that point]

Page 92: Pie Charts

1 a) $\frac{1}{4}$ *[1 mark]*

b) Badminton = 360 − 180 − 90 − 30 = 60°
Football = 180°, so 60 people = 180°
1 person = 180° ÷ 60 = 3°
So number of people who prefer badminton = 60° ÷ 3° = 20
[2 marks available — 1 mark for a correct method, 1 mark for the correct final answer]
There are other ways to work this out — e.g. you could also use the number of people who prefer football (60) to work out the total people surveyed and then use the angle of the badminton sector to work out what fraction of the total this is $\left(\frac{1}{6}\right)$.

2 a) Total number of people = 12 + 18 + 9 + 21 = 60
Multiplier = 360 ÷ 60 = 6
Plain: 12 × 6 = 72°
Salted: 18 × 6 = 108°
Sugared: 9 × 6 = 54°
Toffee: 21 × 6 = 126°

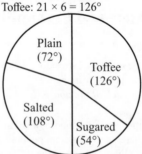

[3 marks available — 1 mark for a correct method, 1 mark for all angles drawn correctly ± 1°, 1 mark for correct labels]

b) E.g. Chris is not right because there is no information about the number of people in the ice-cream survey. *[1 mark]*

Page 93: Scatter Graphs

1 a) positive *[1 mark]*

   b) E.g.

Spanish (%)

   [1 mark for line of best fit that lies between (12, 16) and (12, 28) and also between (80, 82) and (80, 96)]

   c) 56%
   [2 marks available — 1 mark for indicating 66 on the y-axis, 1 mark for the x-coordinate of the line of best fit when y = 66]

2 a)

Height (cm)

   [1 mark for both points plotted correctly]

   b) Cross circled as shown on graph above *[1 mark]*

   c) 72-74 kg
   [2 marks available — 1 mark for line of best fit, 1 mark for an answer in the range 72-74 kg]

Page 94: Stem and Leaf Diagrams

1 a) Median = $(29 + 30) \div 2 = 29.5$ mm *[1 mark]*

   b) Range = $43 - 8 = 35$ mm *[1 mark]*

   c) E.g. The rainfall was much higher in June, as the median was 15.5 mm higher. The amount of rainfall in June was more varied than in November as the range was higher in June.
   [2 marks available — 1 mark for a correct statement comparing the two medians, 1 mark for a correct statement comparing the two ranges]

2 a)
```
14 | 8
15 | 5 8 9 9          Key: 16|2 means 162 cm
16 | 0 2 3 3 4 5 7 9 9 9
17 | 0 1 2 3 5
```
   [3 marks available — 3 marks for a fully correct diagram with a key, otherwise 1 mark for a correct key, and 1 mark for a complete diagram but with the numbers within the 'leaves' in the wrong order]

   b) Modal height = 169 cm *[1 mark]*

   c) Number of students less than 165 cm tall = 10 *[1 mark]*

Page 95: Frequency Tables and Averages

1 a)

Drink	Tally	Frequency
Cola	ЖЖ II	7
Orange juice	ЖЖ	5
Lemonade	III	3
Other	ЖЖ	5

   [2 marks available — 2 marks if all the frequencies are correct, otherwise 1 mark if at least 2 frequencies are correct]

   b) Cola *[1 mark]*

2 a) Total number of vehicles = $13 + 8 + 6 + 2 + 1 = 30$, so the median is halfway between the 15th and 16th values *[1 mark]*, so the median = 1 *[1 mark]*
   [2 marks available in total — as above]

   b) $((13 \times 0) + (8 \times 1) + (6 \times 2) + (2 \times 3) + (1 \times 4)) \div 30$
   $= (0 + 8 + 12 + 6 + 4) \div 30$
   $= 30 \div 30 = 1$
   [3 marks available — 1 mark for multiplying the vehicles per minute by the frequency and adding, 1 mark for dividing by 30, 1 mark for the correct final answer]

Page 96: Grouped Frequency Tables — Averages

1

Arm Span, x cm	Frequency	Mid-Interval Value	Frequency × Mid-Interval Value
$120 \leq x < 130$	13	$(120 + 130) \div 2$ $= 125$	$13 \times 125 =$ 1625
$130 \leq x < 140$	6	$(130 + 140) \div 2$ $= 135$	$6 \times 135 =$ 810
$140 \leq x < 150$	4	$(140 + 150) \div 2$ $= 145$	$4 \times 145 =$ 580
$150 \leq x < 160$	7	$(150 + 160) \div 2$ $= 155$	$7 \times 155 =$ 1085
Total	30		4100

So an estimate of the mean arm span is $4100 \div 30 = 136.6666...$
$= 137$ cm (to the nearest cm.)
[4 marks available — 1 mark for the correct midpoints, 1 mark for using these to find frequency × mid-interval value, 1 mark for 4100 ÷ 30, 1 mark for the correct final answer]

2 a) Total number of children = $3 + 2 + 12 + 8 + 5 = 30$, so the median value is halfway between the 15th and 16th values *[1 mark]*, so it is in the $9.5 \leq x < 10$ group *[1 mark]*
   [2 marks available in total — as above]

   b) $9.5 \leq x < 10$ *[1 mark]*

   c)

Length of line, x cm	Frequency	Mid-Interval Value	Frequency × Mid-Interval Value
$8.5 \leq x < 9$	3	$(8.5 + 9) \div 2 =$ 8.75	$3 \times 8.75 =$ 26.25
$9 \leq x < 9.5$	2	$(9 + 9.5) \div 2 =$ 9.25	$2 \times 9.25 =$ 18.5
$9.5 \leq x < 10$	12	$(9.5 + 10) \div 2$ $= 9.75$	$12 \times 9.75 =$ 117
$10 \leq x < 10.5$	8	$(10 + 10.5) \div 2$ $= 10.25$	$8 \times 10.25 =$ 82
$10.5 \leq x < 11$	5	$(10.5 + 11) \div 2$ $= 10.75$	$5 \times 10.75 =$ 53.75
Total	30		297.5

So an estimate of the mean length is $297.5 \div 30 = 9.9166...$
$= 9.9$ cm (to 1 d.p.)
[4 marks available — 1 mark for the correct midpoints, 1 mark for using these to find frequency × mid-interval value, 1 mark for dividing 297.5 by 30, 1 mark for the correct final answer]

Page 97: Frequency Polygons

1 <u>Time spent on homework in one week</u>

[2 marks available — 2 marks if all 4 points are plotted correctly and joined up, otherwise 1 mark if either the points are correct but not joined up, or if only 2 or 3 points are correct, or if the points have been plotted at the upper or lower class boundaries and joined up]

2 a) E.g. There was between 4 and 6 mm of rainfall more often in Holcombury than in Ramsbrooke.
   [1 mark for any correct comparison]

   There are quite a few other comparisons you could make here — for example, you could look at the total rainfall over the 45 days.

   b) $(3 \times 1) + (5 \times 3) + (6 \times 5) + (13 \times 7) + (11 \times 9) + (6 \times 11) + (1 \times 13) = 3 + 15 + 30 + 91 + 99 + 66 + 13 = 317$
   $317 \div 45 = 7.0444.... = 7.0$ mm (to 1 d.p.)
   [3 marks available — 1 mark for multiplying the frequencies by the midpoints, 1 mark for dividing by 45, 1 mark for the correct final answer]

Pages 98-99: Probability Basics

1 a) unlikely *[1 mark]*
   b) evens *[1 mark]*
   c) impossible *[1 mark]*

2 a)

   [1 mark]

   b)

   [1 mark]

   c) $\frac{2}{6} = \frac{1}{3}$
   [2 marks available — 1 mark for showing there are 2 chances out of 6, 1 mark for the correct simplified fraction]

3 a) Blue *[1 mark]*
   b) $\frac{3}{8}$ *[1 mark]*

4 a) $1 - 0.13 = 0.87$, so the probability she does not complete the walk is 0.87 because probabilities always add to 1.
   [2 marks available — 1 mark for the correct probability, 1 mark for a correct explanation]

   b) E.g. she might give birth to triplets.
   [1 mark for an explanation indicating there are other options]

5 a) Number of red counters = $10 - 4 = 6$ *[1 mark]*
   Probability of getting a red counter = $\frac{6}{10} = \frac{3}{5}$ *[1 mark]*
   [2 marks available in total — as above]

   If the question doesn't tell you how to give your answer, a correct decimal would gain full marks too.

   b) There are no green counters, so the probability of getting a green = 0 *[1 mark]*

6 Total number of people in the team = $6 + 9 + 4 + 1 = 20$ *[1 mark]*
   So the probability that person's favourite position is midfield
   = $\frac{9}{20}$ *[1 mark]*
   [2 marks available in total — as above]

Page 100: More Probability

1 (hockey, netball), (hockey, choir), (hockey, orienteering), (orchestra, netball), (orchestra, choir), (orchestra, orienteering), (drama, netball), (drama, choir), (drama, orienteering)
   [2 marks available — 2 marks if all 9 possible outcomes are correct, otherwise 1 mark if at least 5 are correct]

2 a)

		Cards			
	2	**4**	**6**	**8**	**10**
1	3	5	7	9	11
2	4	6	8	10	12
3	5	7	9	11	13
4	6	8	10	12	14
5	7	9	11	13	15
6	8	10	12	14	16

(Dice labels rows 1–6)

   [2 marks available — 2 marks if all entries are correct, otherwise 1 mark if at least 4 entries are correct]

   b) 3 ways of scoring exactly 9
   Total number of possible outcomes = 30
   Probability of scoring exactly 9 = $\frac{3}{30}$ *[1 mark]* = $\frac{1}{10}$ *[1 mark]*
   [2 marks available in total — as above]

Page 101: Relative Frequency

1 a) $50 \times 0.12 = 6$
   [2 marks available — 1 mark for a correct method, 1 mark for the correct final answer]

   b) 1 and 3 have a much higher relative frequency than the other numbers, so the dice is probably not fair.
   [2 marks available — 1 mark for 'probably not fair' or 'not fair' or 'may not be fair' or similar, 1 mark for an explanation that includes numbers or refers to relative frequency]

   c) She should not expect the same results as there are a large number of possible outcomes all with similar probabilities.
   [1 mark for a correct explanation of why she shouldn't expect the same result]

2 a)

Number on counter	1	2	3	4	5
Frequency	23	25	22	21	9
Relative frequency	0.23	0.25	0.22	0.21	0.09

   [2 marks available — 2 marks for all correct answers, otherwise 1 mark for any frequency ÷ 100]

   b) E.g. No, because the relative frequency for selecting a counter numbered 5 is too low — they should each be around 0.2 if the number of counters is equal.
   [1 mark for saying that he's wrong (or probably wrong) because the relative frequency for 5 is too low]

Page 102: Expected Frequency

1 $200 \times 0.64 = 128$ times
   [2 marks available — 1 mark for a correct method, 1 mark for the correct final answer]

2 $400 \times 0.35 = 140$
   [2 marks available — 1 mark for a correct method, 1 mark for the correct final answer]

3 P(lands on 5) = 1 − P(lands on 1, 2, 3 or 4) *[1 mark]*
   P(lands on 5) = $1 - (0.3 + 0.15 + 0.2 + 0.25) = 0.1$ *[1 mark]*
   Estimate of number of times spinner lands on 5 = 100×0.1 *[1 mark]*
   = 10 times *[1 mark]*
   [4 marks available in total — as above]

Answers